A Promising Addition to the World's Cereal Grains

Report of an Ad Hoc Panel of the
Advisory Committee on Technology Innovation
Board on Science and Technology for International Developmen
National Research Council

in Cooperation with the Board on Agriculture
National Research Council

NATIONAL ACADEMY PRESS
Washington, D.C. 1989

NOTICE: The project that is the subject of this report was approved by the Governing Board of the National Research Council, whose members are drawn from the councils of the National Academy of Sciences, the National Academy of Engineering, and the Institute of Medicine. The members of the committee responsible for the report were chosen for their special competences and with regard for appropriate balance.

This report has been reviewed by a group other than the authors according to procedures approved by a Report Review Committee consisting of members of the National Academy of Sciences, the National Academy of Engineering, and the Institute of Medicine.

The National Academy of Sciences is a private, nonprofit, self-perpetuating society of distinguished scholars engaged in scientific and engineering research, dedicated to the furtherance of science and technology and to their use for the general welfare. Upon the authority of the charter granted to it by the Congress in 1863, the Academy has a mandate that requires it to advise the federal government on scientific and technical matters. Dr. Frank Press is president of the National Academy of Sciences.

The National Academy of Engineering was established in 1964, under the charter of the National Academy of Sciences, as a parallel organization of outstanding engineers. It is autonomous in its administration and in the selection of its members, sharing with the National Academy of Sciences the responsibility for advising the federal government. The National Academy of Engineering also sponsors engineering programs aimed at meeting national needs, encourages education and research, and recognizes the superior achievements of engineers. Dr. Robert M. White is president of the National Academy of Engineering.

The Institute of Medicine was established in 1970 by the National Academy of Sciences to secure the services of eminent members of appropriate professions in the examination of policy matters pertaining to the health of the public. The Institute acts under the responsibility given to the National Academy of Sciences by its congressional charter to be an adviser to the federal government and, upon its own initiative, to identify issues of medical care, research, and education. Dr. Samuel O. Thier is president of the Institute of Medicine.

The National Research Council was organized by the National Academy of Sciences in 1916 to associate the broad community of science and technology with the Academy's purposes of furthering knowledge and advising the federal government. Functioning in accordance with general policies determined by the Academy, the Council has become the principal operating agency of both the National Academy of Sciences and the National Academy of Engineering in providing services to the government, the public, and the scientific and engineering communities. The Council is administered jointly by both Academies and the Institute of Medicine. Dr. Frank Press and Dr. Robert M. White are chairman and vice chairman, respectively, of the National Research Council.

The Board on Science and Technology for International Development (BOSTID) of the Office of International Affairs addresses a range of issues arising from the ways in which science and technology in developing countries can stimulate and complement the complex processes of social and economic development. It oversees a broad program of bilateral workshops with scientific organizations in developing countries and conducts special studies. BOSTID's Advisory Committee on Technology Innovation publishes topical reviews of technical processes and biological resources of potential importance to developing countries.

This report has been prepared by an ad hoc advisory panel of the Advisory Committee on Technology Innovation, Board on Science and Technology for International Development, Office of International Affairs, National Research Council. Staff support was funded by the Office of the Science Advisor, Agency for International Development, under Grant No. DAN 5538-G-SS-1023-00.

Library of Congress Catalog Card Number: 89-42684
ISBN 0-309-04263-1

Cover illustration: G. Hettel, CIMMYT

PANEL ON TRITICALE

WILLIAM L. BROWN, Retired Chairman and President, Pioneer Hi-Bred International, Inc., Johnson, Iowa; and Chairman, Board on Agriculture, The National Research Council, *Chairman*

RICARDO BRESSANI, Head, Division of Food Sciences, Instituto de Nutrición de Centro América y Panamá, Guatemala City, Guatemala

DAVID V. GLOVER, Professor of Plant Genetics and Breeding, Purdue University

ARNEL R. HALLAUER, Research Geneticist, U. S. Department of Agriculture; and Professor of Agronomy, Iowa State University, Ames

VIRGIL A. JOHNSON, Wheat Research Leader, U. S. Department of Agriculture; and Professor of Agronomy, University of Nebraska, Lincoln

CALVIN O. QUALSET, Director of Genetic Resources Conservation Program; and Professor of Agronomy, University of California, Davis

* * *

NOEL D. VIETMEYER, Senior Program Officer, Board on Science and Technology for International Development, *Triticale Study Director* and *Scientific Editor*

National Research Council Staff

F. R. RUSKIN, *BOSTID Editor*
MARY JANE ENGQUIST, *Staff Associate*
MEDGE R. CANSECO, *Administrative Secretary*
ELIZABETH MOUZON, *Senior Secretary*

SPECIAL CONTRIBUTORS

Centro Internacional de Mejoramiento de Maíz y Trigo (CIMMYT)

OSMAN ABDALLA, Breeder, Wheat Program
ARNOLDO AMAYA, Head, Industrial Quality Laboratory
NORMAN BORLAUG, Consultant, Wheat Program
BYRD CURTIS, Head, CIMMYT/Turkey Winter Wheat Program, Ankara, Turkey; Former Director, Wheat Program
GENE HETTEL, Science Writer and Editor, Wheat Information Services
CLIVE JAMES, Former Deputy Director General
ROBERTO PEÑA B., Associate Scientist, Industrial Quality
GENE SAARI, Plant Pathologist, CIMMYT/Turkey Winter Wheat Program, Ankara, Turkey
BENT SKOVMAND, Breeder, Genetic Resources, Wheat Program
GEORGE VARUGHESE, Associate Director, Wheat Program
EVANGELINA VILLEGAS, Head, General Laboratories
DONALD WINKELMANN, Director General

Other Contributors

THOMAS BARKER, Cornell University, Ithaca, New York
RONALD BARNETT, North Florida Research and Education Center, University of Florida, Quincy
CHARLES BENBROOK, Executive Director, Board on Agriculture, National Research Council
ROBERT H. BUSCH, Research Geneticist, U.S. Department of Agriculture Agricultural Research Service, Plant Science Research, Northern States Area, St. Paul, Minnesota
KATHARINE V. COOPER, Department of Agronomy, Waite Agricultural Institute, University of Adelaide, Glen Osmond, Australia
NORMAN L. DARVEY, Plant Breeding Institute, the University of Sydney, New South Wales, Australia
FRED C. ELLIOTT, Triticale Breeder, Yuma, Arizona
GEORGE FEDAK, Cytogenetics Section, Research Station, Research Branch, Agriculture Canada, Ottawa, Ontario
HENRIQUE GUEDES-PINTO, Head, Divisão de Genética e Melhoramento de Plantas, Universidade de Trás-Os-Môntes e Alto Douro, Portugal
J. PERRY GUSTAFSON, Agricultural Research Service, U.S. Department of Agriculture, University of Missouri, Columbia

JOSEPH H. HULSE, International Development Research Centre, Ottawa, Canada

A.R. KLATT, Assistant Dean, International Programs, Oklahoma State University, Stillwater

MATHIAS KOLDING, Cereal Breeder, Columbia Basin Research Center, Hermiston, Oregon

E.N. LARTER, Department of Plant Science, University of Manitoba, Winnipeg, Manitoba, Canada

KLAUS LORENZ, Professor, Department of Food Science and Nutrition, Colorado State University, Fort Collins

ADAM J. LUKASZEWSKI, Department of Agronomy, University of Missouri, Columbia

DONALD R. MARSHALL, Department of Agronomy, Waite Agricultural Institute, University of Adelaide, Glen Osmond, South Australia

TRISTAO MELLO-SAMPAYO, Grupo de Citogenética, Instituto Gulbenkian de Ciência, Oeiras, Portugal

ROBERT J. METZGER, U.S. Department of Agriculture (retired), Corvallis, Oregon

ANASTASIO MORALES, Extension Service, c/o CIANO, Ciudad Obregón, Sonora, Mexico

MIGUEL MOTA, Departamento de Genética, Estacão Agronómica Nacional, Oeiras, Portugal

ROBERT MYER, University of Florida Agricultural Research and Education Center, Marianna

STAN NALEPA, Triticale Breeder, Sun/Seeds Genetics, Inc., Hollister, California

GARY RIESTENBERG, International Nutrition and Genetics Corporation, Perham, Minnesota

DON SALMON, Alberta Agriculture, Lacombe, Alberta, Canada

ERNESTO SAMAYOA, INIFAP, c/o CIANO, Ciudad Obregón, Sonora, Mexico

D. THOMAS SAVAGE, Department of Poultry Science, Oregon State University, Corvallis

ERNEST SEARS, Professor Emeritus of Agronomy, 108 Curtis Hall, University of Missouri, Columbia

LEN SHEBESKI, Department of Plant Science, University of Manitoba, Winnipeg, Canada

ANTONIO VALENCIA, INIFAP, c/o CIANO, Ciudad Obregón, Sonora, Mexico

JEFFREY P. WILSON, U.S. Department of Agriculture, Agricultural Research Service, Coastal Plain Experiment Station, Tifton, Georgia

TADEUSZ WOLSKI, Poznan Plant Breeders, Warsaw, Poland

FRANK J. ZILLINSKY, CYMMYT Triticale Breeder (retired), Gloucester, Ontario, Canada

Preface

The main purpose of this report is to review the status of the types of triticale developed at the Centro Internacional de Mejoramiento de Maíz y Trigo (CIMMYT) as food crops for use in developing nations. A secondary purpose is to reintroduce triticale to the research community outside the Third World. A brief discussion of the crop's future for the United States is given in Appendix A.

To concentrate on CIMMYT's high-yielding, broadly adapted spring triticales seems justified in a book aimed primarily at helping developing countries. It is CIMMYT's types of triticales with good quality for baking that are most likely to benefit Africa, Asia, and Latin America. This is not to say, however, that we intend to slight or ignore the work conducted in Canada, the United States, the Soviet Union, Poland, other European nations, Australia, or anywhere else. The report refers to such work at various points, but it is not intended to be an encyclopedic appraisal of all triticale research.

The panel that produced the report was made up largely of cereal scientists not involved in triticale work. Before they met, most panel members were skeptical of triticale's potential as a crop and were unfamiliar with the details of CIMMYT's recent accomplishments. They met in April 1986 in Ciudad Obregón as well as at the CIMMYT headquarters near Mexico City. For several days they interviewed CIMMYT researchers (see list of CIMMYT contributors), analyzed the latest results, and examined test plots of the current triticale varieties. National Research Council staff then solicited comments and information from other researchers worldwide (see list of other contributors) and integrated the responses into the final report.

The report is intended mainly for officials and institutions concerned with agriculture in developing countries, and scientists with related interests. Its purpose is to provide a general introduction to the crop. It is not a technical guide for introducing, planting, or utilizing triticale. Information on such operational details can be obtained through the research contacts and selected readings given in the appendixes.

This study is a joint effort of two divisions of the National Research

Council: the Board on Agriculture and the Board on Science and Technology for International Development (BOSTID). It continues a BOSTID series that explores promising plant resources that heretofore have been neglected or overlooked. This series is prepared under the auspices of BOSTID's Advisory Committee on Technology Innovation (ACTI). Established in 1971, ACTI's mandate is to assess unconventional scientific and technological advances with particular promise for solving problems of developing countries.

Other titles in ACTI's plant sciences series include:

- *Tropical Legumes: Resources for the Future* (1979)
- *The Winged Bean: A High-Protein Crop for the Tropics* (1981)
- *Amaranth: Modern Prospects for an Ancient Crop* (1983)
- *Quality-Protein Maize* (1988)
- *Lost Crops of the Incas* (1989)

The panel members are indebted to the CIMMYT staff for their assistance and hospitality, as well as for the yield information and other basic data on which this report's conclusions are based. The panel is also grateful to all the contributors, who added immeasurably to the final product.

Funds for this study were made available by the Agency for International Development. Specifically, they were jointly contributed by the Office of the Science Advisor and by the Office of Agriculture in the Bureau for Science and Technology.

How to cite this report:
National Research Council. 1989. *Triticale: A Promising Addition to the World's Cereal Grains*. National Academy Press, Washington, D.C.

Contents

1
Introduction

Coping with tomorrow's unstable weather could become one of the most serious challenges for agriculture. Global warming could summon more floods, droughts, even cold snaps in some regions. Governments should encourage crop diversification to cushion their populations against the shock of climate change.

SURESH SINHA
Indian Agricultural Research Institute

The main food crops of the world were all selected at least 3,000 years ago by people with only Stone Age knowledge and facilities. Now, however, there is a new crop with high potential that could become a major staple—a man-made crop, developed during the last 100 years. Called triticale (usually pronounced trit-i-*kay*-lee), it is still little known, but in the future it, too, could become a staple worldwide.

Triticale is a hybrid resulting from crossing a wheat "mother" with a rye "father." It combines many of the best qualities of both its prodigious parents. It can have most of wheat's qualities for making various types of noodles, pastries, and some breads; and it can have most of rye's disease resistance, drought tolerance, hardiness, and adaptability to "difficult" soils.

Triticale was first deliberately produced in 1876, and even 20 years ago scientists in several countries grew varieties that appeared to have considerable commercial promise. To many observers at that point the plant seemed a modern miracle, and in the 1960s it was planted on thousands of hectares. However, the types then available set seed poorly, their grains were small and shriveled, and their yields were generally disappointing. To make matters worse, in some countries promoters exaggerated the crop's potential, and their claims could not be refuted easily because almost no funds were being committed to triticale research. When word spread that some farmers had been "burned," triticale got a bad reputation.

This reputation was not justified. By the late 1970s, despite a lack of funds, a few dedicated researchers were overcoming many of triticale's technical limitations; indeed, some of their varieties were outyielding the best wheats. But by then the world was glutted with wheat, and virtually no one was interested in planting or buying any newfangled grain. Thus, triticale seemed doubly doomed to obscurity.[1] All over the world it was abandoned.

Nevertheless, a few diehards remained convinced that one day the newborn crop would contribute significantly to global food needs. Some of them were in Canada, the first country to value the plant's modern promise.[2] Others were in Eastern Europe. Those countries, too, had been triticale pioneers, and several of them, particularly Poland, retained healthy triticale development programs. Nonetheless, it is in Mexico that the largest program to breed triticales for human consumption has survived into the present.

Near Mexico City and at Ciudad Obregón in the northern state of Sonora, the Centro Internacional de Mejoramiento de Maíz y Trigo (CIMMYT) has maintained intensive triticale research in its laboratories and fields since 1964. It has concentrated exclusively on breeding triticales for cultivation in developing regions of Africa, Asia, and Latin America. The results have been substantial, and CIMMYT varieties, together with those of some European and American researchers, have led several countries to adopt triticale as a grain crop once again. The decade of the 1980s thus has brought renewed interest in this man-made plant with a roller-coaster history.

THE CHANGING AGRICULTURAL SCENE

In one sense, the crop and its moment are coming together. Triticale seems to be the type of robust crop that will contribute more to world agriculture in the future than it has in the past. This is because the time ahead is one of uncertainty and of almost certain change.

In the immediate future, for example, ecological, biological, technological, economic, and social conditions all seem more likely to fluctuate than ever before. To cope with such changes, the world will increasingly need highly adaptable crops. Starting soon, consistency of yield under fluctuating conditions may be as important as maximum yield under ideal conditions.

The causes of the expected changes are discussed below.

---

[1] In some countries, the plant remained as a crop for green forage and hay. However, this report concentrates on triticale's potential as a cereal grain for human consumption.
[2] The University of Manitoba had initiated triticale research in 1954 and retained a substantial program until 1981, when its funds were summarily terminated. Small programs survived in Alberta and Ontario.

Population Increases

The most significant force driving the coming changes is the rising number of people in the Third World. World population, currently 5.2 billion, has doubled since 1952 and will increase by almost 25 percent by the close of this century. The great majority of the 1.2 billion expected newcomers will be added to developing countries where even now ballooning population is pushing the slender reserves of arable land to the brink of exhaustion. And after the turn of the century, the situation will probably worsen. By the year 2025, for example, world population may grow by three billion. Just to sustain today's level of nourishment, food production will have to grow by 50 percent by then. In addition, if rising expectations are to be met and if food is to be provided for the millions who are currently malnourished, the increase will have to be even greater.

Limits to Agriculture

In the past, food production has been increased by modifying sites and soils to suit the needs of the dozen or so major crops. Drylands have been irrigated, wetlands drained, sloping lands terraced, barren lands fertilized, tropical forests felled, and pest-prone sites sprayed with chemicals. By these methods, supplemented with plant breeding to bring out the highest potentials within crop species, world food production has been raised to a stunning extent. Because of this, local famines notwithstanding, the massive famines widely predicted in the 1960s never materialized.

But the processes of the past three decades seem to be reaching their limits. The so-called Green Revolution, in which genetics, fertilizers, and modern agricultural techniques are employed to maximize crop yields, is in danger of running out of steam. India, for example, more than tripled its wheat harvest between 1965 (the start of the Green Revolution) and 1983, but has barely increased its grain output since.

There are several reasons for the slowdown. Not only is the prime agricultural land almost fully exploited, but the productivity of some of it is actually decreasing. Sprawling cities and villages are shrinking the area for growing crops, particularly the expanses needed for grain fields. Erosion is thinning topsoil and sometimes exposing toxic underlayers. Fertilizers and acid rain are increasing soil acidity and releasing free aluminum, which is toxic to today's conventional food crops. And pests are becoming increasingly resistant to various pesticides, which are also increasing in price and causing much public concern.

Moreover, not only is the old land almost fully exploited, but there are limits to the amount of new land that can be converted into prime farming areas. On every front, the possibility for bringing additional land under cultivation is extremely limited. For example, the potential for establishing new large-scale irrigation schemes is diminishing as industry and cities compete with farmers for dwindling supplies of water. (In fact, some irrigated land is going out of production because of the needs of cities and the buildup of salts that kill crops.) The amount of wetland that can be drained in future is being sharply reduced as the disruptive effects on wildlife and environment become more apparent. The same can be said about the amount of tropical forests that can be felled to provide farmland.

Climatic Change

The droughts that gripped the United States and China in the summer of 1988 have focused attention on a possibly deteriorating world climatic situation. Signs are ominous and appear to point to a warming trend. The 1980s have been the warmest decade in a century. The years 1980, 1981, 1983, 1987, and 1988 were unusually hot all over the world; 1987 was the hottest year on record. Based on today's trends, a rise in the earth's temperature of at least 1°C seems inevitable by the middle of the twenty-first century.

As a result of these trends, which may be associated with the intensification of the greenhouse effect, it seems likely that in the future most countries will experience more extreme weather conditions than in the past. This could affect world food production. Indeed, climates for growing today's food crops could shift, perhaps to regions where soils are too poor to support the yields necessary for feeding the planet.

CROPS OF THE FUTURE

Because of the limits to intensive agriculture and the probable climatic changes, future growth in world food output will not come easily. While some of the new human arrivals will be fed by yield increases on existing land, most will have to survive on sites that are now considered inappropriate for intensive agriculture. In future, arable cropping will have to expand onto increasingly marginal lands.

Therefore, to avoid disasters of global proportions, the world must develop an arsenal of techniques to help make today's marginal lands part of tomorrow's breadbaskets. One of these techniques is the development of crops that are vigorous, dependable, and "self-reliant."

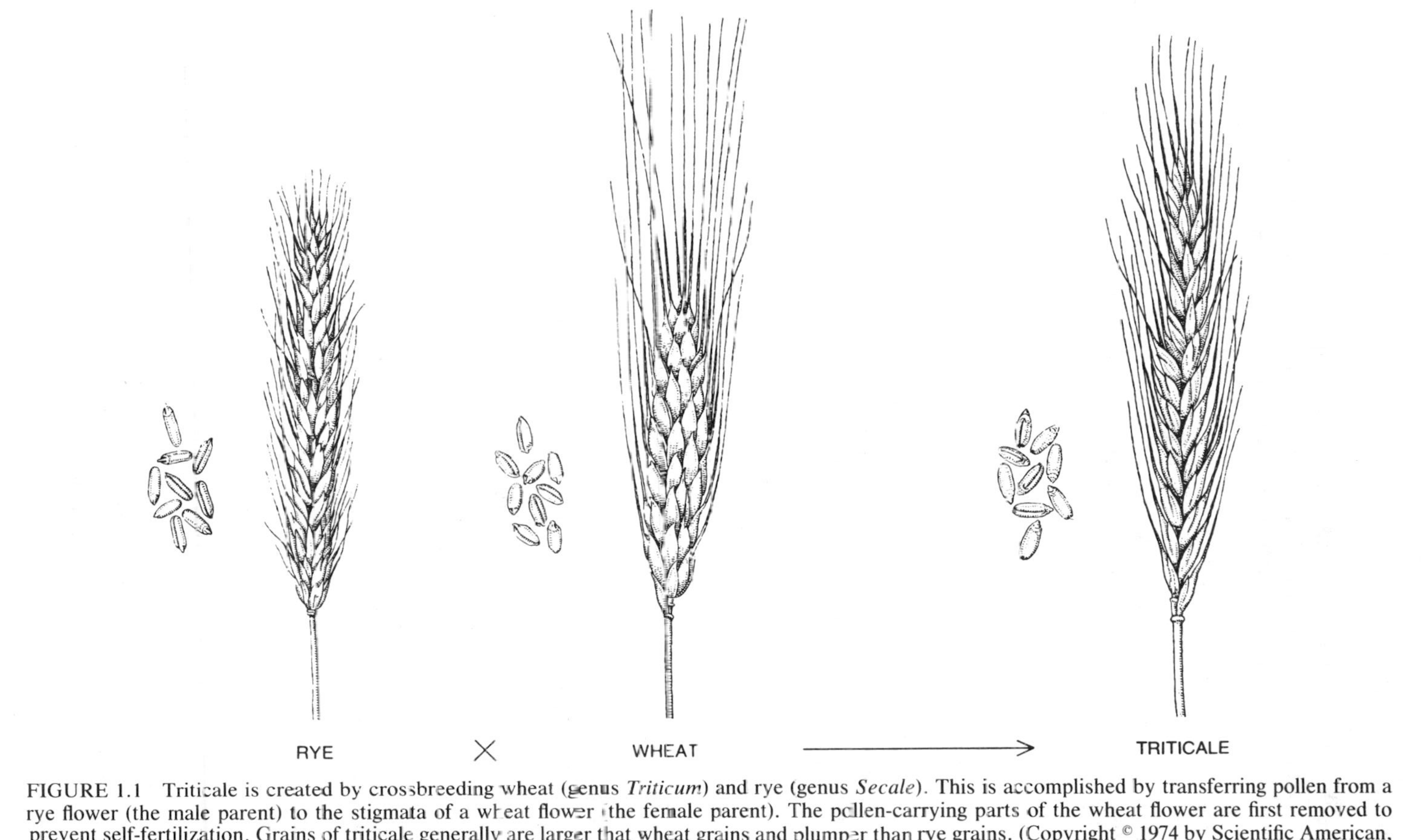

FIGURE 1.1 Triticale is created by crossbreeding wheat (genus *Triticum*) and rye (genus *Secale*). This is accomplished by transferring pollen from a rye flower (the male parent) to the stigmata of a wheat flower (the female parent). The pollen-carrying parts of the wheat flower are first removed to prevent self-fertilization. Grains of triticale generally are larger that wheat grains and plumper than rye grains. (Copyright © 1974 by Scientific American, Inc. All rights reserved)

Such crops should yield well with low inputs on substandard soils where today's crops grow poorly—crops that can withstand fluctuating environmental conditions without slumping in production.

It is for this reason that triticale is potentially important. By and large, this plant makes better use of suboptimal soils and (at least when compared with wheat) requires fewer inputs of fertilizer, lime, and pesticides. It holds promise of high performance in sites where wheat, in particular, performs poorly. This is because it has the genetic endowment of its rye "father."

Rye

In the union that makes triticale, rye is the source of pollen. A relative newcomer among foods, rye probably originated in southwestern Asia and attracted little attention before 1000 B.C., when its cultivation began both in Central Europe and in Britain. Today, it is one of the world's principal cereals, although it ranks only seventh in volume of production.[3]

Rye's outstanding quality is its robustness. In poorer environments, it grows better than most other cereals. Indeed, it probably first forced itself on the attention of farmers as a vigorous, irrepressible invader of their wheat fields. Soon, however, those ancient farmers came to appreciate its vitality.[4] Rye prospers on soils so infertile or acidic that wheat fails; it flourishes in colder climates—farther north (as far as the Arctic Circle) and higher up mountainsides (up to elevations above 4,000 m in Central Asia)—than wheat. On poor sites its yields may be low, but they are almost always higher than wheat's. Because of this ability to withstand harsh environments, it is normally relegated to the worst soils and the most unfavorable conditions. As a result, rye became known as a "grain of poverty."

"Grains of poverty" are exactly what are needed to expand food production on marginal soils. But like all crops, rye has its own problems. It is afflicted by poor pollination. It is susceptible to ergot, a fungal disease that can be toxic to people who eat it. Its grain contains at least one substance that reduces the growth of pigs and

---

[3] The exact extent of rye production is uncertain because the largest producer, the Soviet Union, publishes no figures. It is believed to grow 40 percent of the world's rye—around 9 million hectares; Poland grows around 2.5 million hectares.

[4] Rye's hardiness was important to colonial North America. The earliest settlers planted the crop in Virginia and New England on roughly cleared land often studded with tree stumps. At first it grew poorly. Wheat, however, was even worse, succumbing to rust. Rye succeeded better and more quickly. For two centuries American breads were made with rye, oats, barley, and maize—sometimes mixed with a little wheat, but more often combined only with each other.

chickens. (These substances are not a problem for humans because they are inactivated by heat—for example, when bread is baked.)

Moreover, rye grain is far less popular than wheat. Like bread wheat, it contains elastic protein of the type that makes breads rise, but its flour does not rise as well as wheat flour. Nonetheless, it produces flavorful leavened breads—the dark breads and pumpernickels of Central Europe, for instance. Indeed, for breadmaking, rye is the world's second most important grain.

Wheat

In the union that makes triticale, wheat is the source of egg cells. It is a prestigious heritage. Wheat ranks first among all the world's cereals.[5] It is our most extensive crop, the basic foodstuff for a billion people in 45 countries. More land is given over to it—about 260 million hectares in all—than to any other crop. Annual production is now more than 500 million metric tons.

Wheat is produced almost exclusively for human consumption. In developing and developed countries combined, it now furnishes 20 percent of calories and 45 percent of protein—as much protein as is derived from all the meat, milk, and eggs consumed.

The wheat plant is remarkably adaptable, but for all that, it is best suited to temperate regions, to annual rainfalls between 300 and 900 mm, and to compact but well-drained soils. It is not a good crop for many marginal lands or sites subject to climatic fluctuations. For instance, it is poorly adapted to highly acid soils, highly alkaline soils, and to regions with droughts or extremes of heat or cold.

Of the several types, the two most important are the durum wheats and common wheats. Durum wheats generally have hard grains and stiff and inelastic proteins, which make them unsuitable for breadmaking. They are used to make spaghetti, macaroni, and other pastas, as well as soda crackers.

Common wheats have soft to hard grains as a result of differing proportions of various proteins. Soft types have weak elastic proteins and are used in pastries, breakfast cereals, noodles, and other unleavened foods. Hard types generally contain a strong elastic protein (gluten) that helps retain the carbon dioxide gas, generated from yeast or baking powder, that enables bread to rise. They are used to make breads and other baked products. Despite their several uses, common wheats are generally called "bread wheats."

[5] Wheat, rice, maize, sorghum, barley, oats, and rye.

2
History

Triticale is a product of a century of dreams and forty years of active pursuit of the all-but-impossible.

B. S. DODGE
It Started in Eden

TRITICALE'S BEGINNINGS

In fields where wheat and rye grow in proximity, cross-pollination sometimes—although rarely—occurs. The two plants were first deliberately crossed by Alexander Stephen Wilson. In 1876, in his greenhouse in Scotland, this amateur botanist took pollen from rye plants and used it to fertilize wheat flowers. The hybrid plants he grew from the resulting seeds were exciting to biologists, but were uninteresting to farmers because they could not reproduce themselves. It is now known that wheat and rye imparted their chromosomes to those seeds, but that these incompatible chromosomes could not pair up. Thus, although the hybrid produced egg and pollen cells, it remained sterile.

The first indication that this line of investigation might not be a dead end came in 1891 when a German botanist, Wilhelm Rimpau, succeeded in finding a natural wheat/rye hybrid that was partially fertile. Several decades later, in the 1920s and 1930s, Soviet and Swedish researchers attempted to develop this and similar specimens into crops.[1] Elsewhere, however, the fact that rye pollen could fertilize wheat flowers remained an academic curiosity.

The next fundamental advance came in 1937 when botanists learned that colchicine (a natural chemical extracted from the autumn crocus

[1] The Soviet work was stimulated by the remarkable occurrence of a "swarm" of thousands of hybrids that appeared in wheat plots at the Agricultural Experiment Station of Saratov in 1918. To prevent cross-pollination, the wheat plots had been separated from each other by rows of rye plants. In one plot, as much as 20 percent of the grains on the wheat plants were hybrids. This work, by G. K. Meister, was suddenly stopped in the 1930s when he "disappeared," charged with not fulfilling his overly optimistic projections for the new hybrids.

plant) can "double" the chromosomes in newly forming cells.[2] This opened new vistas: in the cells of the man-made, sterile, hybrid seedlings, chromosomes of both wheat and rye could be artificially doubled into pairs so that the meiotic cells could proceed with normal reduction division. From then on, making triticale fertile no longer depended on Rimpau's seeds or natural chance.

By 1938, Swedish plant geneticist Arne Müntzing applied the colchicine treatment to his own wheat/rye hybrids and found that it transformed them into plants that produced viable seeds.

Neither a wheat nor a rye, this was a new plant. Its common name had been coined from *Triticum* and *Secale*, the scientific names for the respective genera of wheat and rye.[3] It varies in appearance depending on the varieties of wheat and rye used to make it. Generally, however, it looks like wheat; from a distance, triticale fields resemble wheat fields. Only close inspection shows that most of the plants have a covering of soft velvety hairs just below the seed head ("hairy neck"); long, droopy spikes; and long beards (awns)—a characteristic of rye but of few wheats.

The first triticales were made using bread wheats.[4] The results are called "octoploids" because they have eight sets of chromosomes: bread wheat's six combined with rye's two (chapter 5). A different type of triticale was created in 1948 when Joseph G. O'Mara crossed a durum wheat with rye.[5] This produced "hexaploid" triticales that have six sets of chromosomes: durum wheat's four combined with rye's two. At present, these triticales appear to hold more promise than the octoploids, and they are the main subject of this report.

MIDDLE PERIOD

The current interest in triticale had its origins in Canada. In 1954, L. H. Shebeski and B. C. Jenkins of the University of Manitoba gathered triticale specimens from researchers around the world. Their goal was to use triticale as a bridge for transferring rye's natural resistance to leaf diseases into Canada's durum-wheat crop.

---

[2] The discovery that colchicine alters cell division was made in 1889 by Italian botanist B. Pernice, but its implications lay unappreciated for almost 50 years. Information from O.J. Eigsti.

[3] The name was devised in 1935 by the Austrian plant breeder Erich Tschermak-Seysenegg, one of the rediscoverers of Mendel's laws of genetics and the person who "created" naked-seed pumpkin.

[4] For example, those of Müntzing, Rimpau, Meister, and another Soviet plant breeder, V. Pissarev.

[5] O'Mara began the work at the University of Missouri and continued it at Iowa State University.

During this period of the 1950s and 1960s, a few European researchers were also exploring triticales. In Spain, Enrique Sanchez-Monge developed a variety (Cachirulo) that was released for production in 1969. In Hungary, Arpad Kiss developed triticales so successfully that in 1969 Hungarian farmers planted 40,000 hectares of them, mainly for animal feed.

In the mid 1960s, researchers were starting to feel good about the crop and its potential, and the University of Manitoba and CIMMYT established a joint program to develop triticales for use in developing countries.[6] In Mexico, CIMMYT researchers[7] began testing the Canadian lines. In the research plots where the famous Green Revolution wheats had been developed, the results were disappointing. At Ciudad Obregón and Toluca, the triticales—some of which in Canada occasionally equaled the best wheat yields—failed to produce more than half as much grain as the best Mexican wheats. Magnificent-looking plants—some surpassed wheat in total green matter—their grain yields were depressed by late maturity, diseases, lodging (the tendency to fall over), seed shriveling, and the failure of many flowers to produce seed because the hybrid sterility had not been fully overcome.

In an effort to overcome these limitations, many of those early triticales were crossbred with each other as well as with bread wheats. This produced promising new types that began to attract favorable attention in several parts of the world. Indeed, the crop's performance appeared so promising that it soon stimulated much press attention and enthusiastic promotion.

Those early triticales were exceptionally nutritious: their grains contained far more protein and lysine (an essential amino acid vital to human health) than wheat. The time was one in which famine and a "global protein gap" were major world concerns, and the new crop seemed to offer a miraculous solution. One researcher predicted that by about 1990, "triticale will have begun to compete seriously with the bread wheats as one of the world's most important food crops."

This might well have happened, but the first commercial triticales were primitive and in practice proved to have many agronomic deficiencies, including:

Low grain yields. They averaged only about half the yield of the wheats grown beside them for comparison.

Poor seed set. Many florets failed to produce seeds, so that fields that looked extremely productive often yielded little grain.

[6] The triticale work was actually initiated in 1964 under the Office of Special Studies of the Rockefeller Foundation. CIMMYT was formed out of this organization in 1966.
[7] Notably, Norman Borlaug, Joseph Ruppert, and Ricardo Rodrigues.

Shriveled grain. Instead of the smooth, plump grains typical of wheat, they had wrinkled, lusterless seeds with deep creases.

Poor adaptation. The same seeds planted in various locations under different climatic conditions proved notably different in agronomic performance.

Excessive height. The plants were tall and weak; storms easily knocked them down.

Premature sprouting. In humid climates many grains often sprouted while still on the mother plant.

Low germination. The shrunken, malformed seed germinated poorly when planted.

Lack of tillering. The plants seldom produced more than one seed-bearing shoot.

Disease susceptibility. The resistance to stripe rust—a disease widespread in many cool, moist, wheat-growing regions—was low.

Late maturity. Because they had been developed in Canada where summer days are long, they performed badly when grown at tropical latitudes where days are short. When planted in the fall, they took so long to flower that the stress of early summer heat caused their grains to fill out poorly. Planted in the spring or summer, they sometimes could not mature their grain before fall frosts killed the plants—especially at high elevation sites. Moreover, daylength sensitivity made it difficult to grow more than one crop in a year.

Low baking quality. Weak gluten, often made worse by premature sprouting of the grain, prevented dough from rising into the light, fluffy breads that most consumers prefer.

To most observers, this massive combination of difficulties seemed a barrier that could never be breached. The field performance was unacceptable to farmers; the grain's appearance was unacceptable to grain merchants, the low flour yield was unacceptable to millers,[8] and the poor baking properties were unacceptable to bakers. It is understandable, therefore, that almost everyone concluded that triticale was a "flash-in-the-pan," unworthy of any further consideration. In the mid–1970s, a backlash arose as rapidly as the enthusiasm of a few years earlier. Disenchanted farmers and agricultural companies quickly

---

[8] While one hectoliter of standard bread wheats weighed 77 kg (or 60 lb per bushel), one hectoliter of triticale in the 1960s typically weighed only 60–70 kg (or 47-54 lb per bushel).

discarded the new cereal. Most universities and other research institutions dropped all triticale work from their roster of research. The crop that had once had so much promise now seemed dead.

MODERN HISTORY

Despite disappointment in the plant's performance, a few researchers refused to despair. For example, in Mexico a handful of CIMMYT wheat scientists[9] maintained the viable triticale research program. Their goal was to eliminate the plant's undesirable traits and to make it into a food crop for poor people in poor countries.

A breakthrough, which had previously occurred in one of CIMMYT's nurseries, proved to be crucial. In 1967, a woebegone triticale plant was accidentally fertilized by pollen blown in from nearby plots of dwarf bread wheats. After a few generations of selection it resulted in a new breeding line called Armadillo.[10] This new triticale had better fertility (seed set); also, its yield was high, it was insensitive to daylength, it was short and stiff-strawed, it matured early, and its grain was only slightly shriveled. Thus, in one fell swoop, Armadillo helped resolve many of triticale's agronomic problems.

Later, it was discovered that these traits were stable and heritable, and that Armadillo could be backcrossed readily with both wheats and ryes. As a result, this accident of nature rejuvenated prospects for the crop. By 1970 practically every triticale at CIMMYT included Armadillo in its pedigree, and around the world the few remaining triticale breeders incorporated Armadillo materials into their own strains with renewed hope.

Encouraged by this breakthrough, two Canadian organizations[11] funded a 5-year program at CIMMYT and the University of Manitoba to develop triticales for use in Third World regions. As a result, CIMMYT and Canadian researchers set out to produce high-yielding lines with semidwarf habit and straw stiff enough to withstand windstorms and to accept high levels of fertilization without lodging.

To ensure that future lines would have built-in adaptability, the international collaborators transferred genes for daylength insensitivity from Mexican bread wheats into their triticales. Moreover, they shuttled the seeds of successive generations from a winter crop at

[9] Notably Frank Zillinsky (CIMMYT's first full-time triticale breeder), George Varughese, Bent Skovmand, and Mohan Kohli.

[10] Pronounced, in the Spanish manner, "ar-ma-*dee*-yoh." Most of CIMMYT's triticale families are named after animals.

[11] The International Development Research Centre and the Canadian International Development Agency.

THE BREAKTHROUGH

I must tell you that the largest and most important step toward making the breakthrough in triticale improvement was executed by capricious mother nature herself, one early March morning in 1967 in Ciudad Obregón, Sonora, while scientific man was still in bed. One promiscuous, venturesome stray wheat pollen grain with a potent and valuable "genetic load" from the nearby wheat breeding plots floated across the road under cover of darkness and fertilized a sad but permissive tall, sterile, degenerate triticale plant.

A year later (two generations), scientific men identified several unusually promising plants in a segregating population. The genetic makeup of those plants clearly indicated the value of the illicit stray wheat pollen grain. Its triticale progeny indicated that in the act of fertilization it had created dwarfs, introduced partial photoperiodic insensitivity, and completely overcome the sterility barrier, which had inhibited progress in triticale improvement for decades.

NORMAN BORLAUG, 1969

Ciudad Obregón (near sea level, fertile environment, latitude 27°N) to a summer crop at Toluca (high elevation, less fertile, latitude 19°N) and even to Manitoba, Canada (latitude 50°N). Only those lines able to thrive at every site were retained. All were based on the "miraculous" Armadillo, but this back-and-forth shuttling created breeding pressures that enhanced the subsequent lines' genetic variability, particularly their adaptability to differing soil types, soil fertilities, temperature regimes, photoperiods, rainfalls, and diseases.

Along with this selection for field performance, CIMMYT's food-quality laboratory selected lines that also performed well in foodstuffs, such as raised breads.

In less than a decade, the resultant gene pool contained many triticales that would grow well under a wide array of different environments. There were also lines with good handling qualities, hard and soft seeds, and improved gluten and breadmaking qualities.

Enthusiasm began to rise once again. The plant had been transformed, and by the end of the 1970s triticales were being tested in 400 locations in 83 countries. The once maligned crop was coming back for a second chance.

3
Triticale Today

In less than half a century, triticale has developed from a theoretical curiosity to a new and practical cereal. It is true that a large amount of work will be needed for the production of improved strains with higher value and usability than the material now available. However, it is justified to state that the threshold now has been passed and that triticale is here to stay.

ARNE MÜNTZING, 1979.

As a result of hundreds of trials in scores of countries during the 1980s, triticale is now becoming understood. Indeed, it is establishing itself as a crop worldwide. Although accurate estimates are difficult to obtain, a good guess is that this man-made plant is currently growing on more than 1.5 million hectares in 32 nations (see table 3.1). Of these, however, five or six countries constitute most of the area, a dozen or so arc in the initial stages of introducing the crop, and the remainder are involved merely in exploratory trials. Also, little of the production is yet being used for human food; most is going to livestock.

Nonetheless, even in these formative years, triticale has arisen extremely quickly to become a commercial reality in several nations (see chapter 7). Poland, probably the world's largest producer, has close to 600,000 hectares under cultivation. France, which started planting triticale commercially only in 1980, now plants 300,000 hectares annually. The Soviet Union has at least 250,000 hectares, mainly in the Black Sea region. Other European nations with large triticale plantings include Portugal (80,000 hectares), Spain (30,000 hectares), Italy (15,000 hectares), and Hungary (5,000 hectares).

Among non-European countries, Australia has in recent years cultivated about 160,000 hectares, mainly because triticale is more productive than wheat or barley on acid soils. The grain is at prcsent mostly exported to Asia for poultry feed.

The United States has about 60,000 hectares under triticale, primarily in Texas and the Midwest. These are harvested mostly for forage (see Appendix A), but triticale-based pancake mixes and crackers are gaining supporters because of their savory, nutty flavor. They are sold

TABLE 3.1 World Distribution of Triticale.

Country	Growth Habit*	Area (hectares)
Argentina[a]	S	10,000
Australia[b]	S	160,000
Austria[c]	W	1,000
Belgium[a]	W	5,000
Brazil[a]	S	30,000
Bulgaria[a]	W	10,000
Canada[b]	S + W	6,500
Chile	S	5,000
China[a]	S + W	25,000
France[c]	S + W	300,000
Germany (West)[c]	W	30,000
Greece	S	-
Hungary[a]	W	5,000
India[b]	S	500
Italy[a]	S	15,000
Kenya	S	-
Luxemburg[a]	W	400
Madagascar	S	-
Mexico[a]	S	8,000
The Netherlands[b]	W	1,000
New Zealand[b]	S + W	150
Pakistan	S	-
Poland[b]	W	600,000
Portugal[b]	S	80,000
South Africa[a]	S + W	15,000
Soviet Union[a]	W	250,000
Spain[a]	S	30,000
Switzerland[b]	W	5,000
Tanzania[b]	S	400
Tunisia[b]	S	25,000
United Kingdom[c]	W	16,000
United States[a]	S + W	60,000
Total		1,693,950

* S: Spring type
W: Winter type
[a] Estimate
[b] CIMMYT Survey
[c] Suijs, 1986

SOURCE: Varughese et al., 1986.

widely in specialty food stores. In fact, North American consumers pay a premium for triticale in bread and snacks.

Although the current production is mainly in highly industrialized countries, there is rising interest in Asia, Africa, and Latin America. China is planting approximately 25,000 hectares annually. In North Africa, cultivation is well established in Tunisia (25,000 hectares) and has begun in Morocco. In several other African countries, scientists are gaining experience with the crop in preparation for commercial production. Brazil has 30,000 hectares devoted to triticale, and Argentina—although it had only 1,000 hectares as recently as 1978—now has about 10,000 hectares.

Although most of the world's triticale is currently used as feed grain or forage, the widespread use of the grain in human foods seems to be just around the corner. Indeed, it is already beginning to catch on. As noted, some is sold in gourmet food stores in North America, and a proportion of the crop is also being used as human food in Europe, Mexico, Brazil, Australia, and a few other countries (see figure 3.5).

Already, Mexico is growing 8,000 hectares of triticale, primarily for food. About 4,000 farmers, mainly on impoverished farms in the state of Michoacan, rely on the crop. The state government supports a bakery that daily makes thousands of loaves of whole-grain triticale bread. Also, farmers are adopting triticale for making tortillas in their homes. Triticale flour, they say, produces a tortilla that is softer and more flexible than a wheat tortilla.

STATUS OF THE PLANT

As a result of these experiences in many diverse countries, it is now obvious that the research of the last few years has brought a remarkable turnabout in triticale's features. Most of the technical limitations that formerly hindered the plant have been overcome. Overall, triticale's breadmaking qualities, fertility, kernel type, yields, and field performance are reaching levels normally expected in a cereal crop for widespread use. These are described below.[1]

Breadmaking

In unleavened bread triticale behaves like soft-wheat flour, and the breadmaking process needs no modification. This makes the crop especially promising in many countries of Asia, Africa, and Latin America, where famine and malnutrition exist and the staple is some form of unleavened flat bread—tortillas, chapatis, or *enjera*, for instance.

In leavened breads triticale has not previously been able to match bread wheat. But one of the most important advances—in just the last few years—has been CIMMYT's transformation of triticale's performance in the making of raised breads.

[1] Of course there are exceptions to these generalized statements, depending on the place and the wheat and triticale varieties being compared. No crop gives maximum performance at all locations.

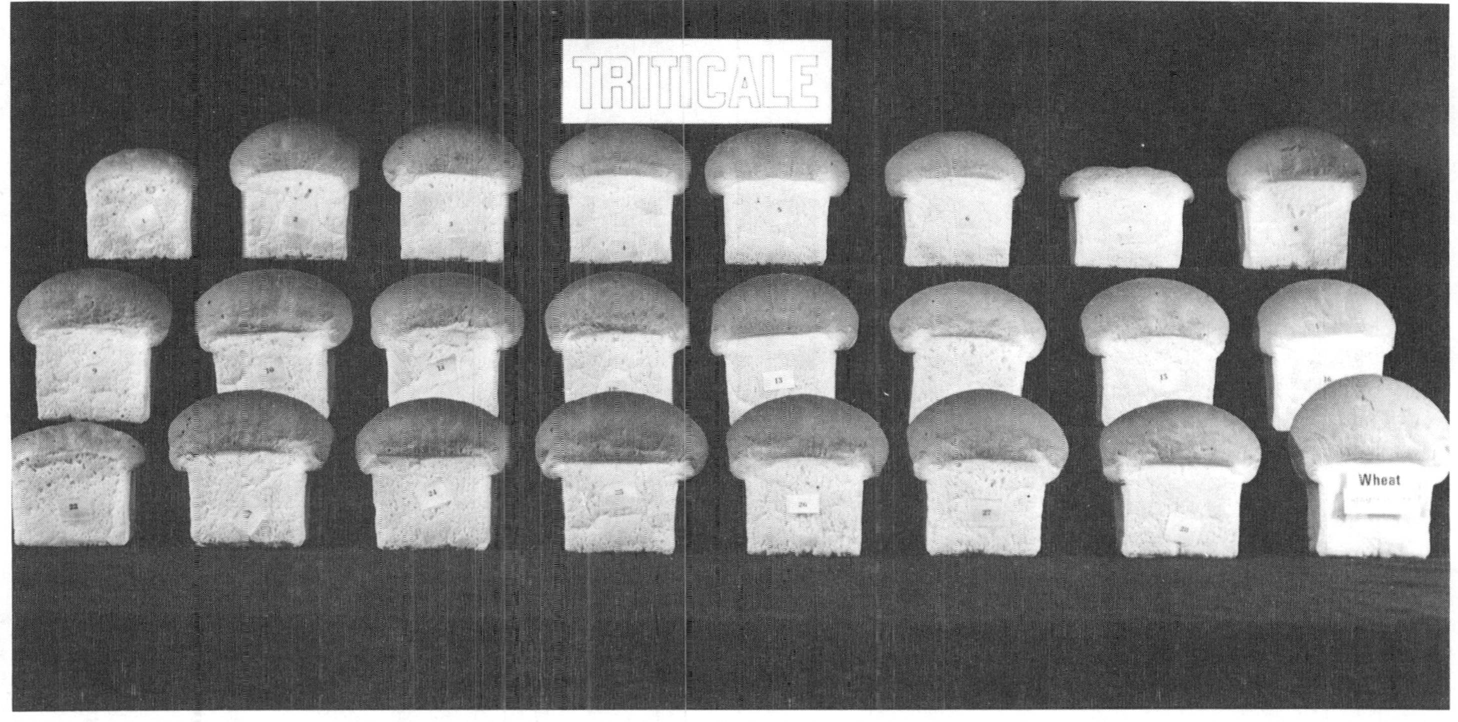

FIGURE 3.1 Although leavened bread is probably the most universal single food, only two grains—wheat and rye—can be used to make it. Now there is an addition to this elite group: triticale.

Triticale flour does not rise quite as much as wheat flour in leavened breads. Nonetheless, by slightly modifying the baking procedures, researchers in Mexico and France have been able to make acceptable raised breads using pure triticale flour. With standard baking procedures, normal loaves can be prepared using a 50:50 mixture of triticale flour and wheat flour. The picture shows loaves made with 23 different triticale varieties and one wheat (lower right) for comparison. (CIMMYT)

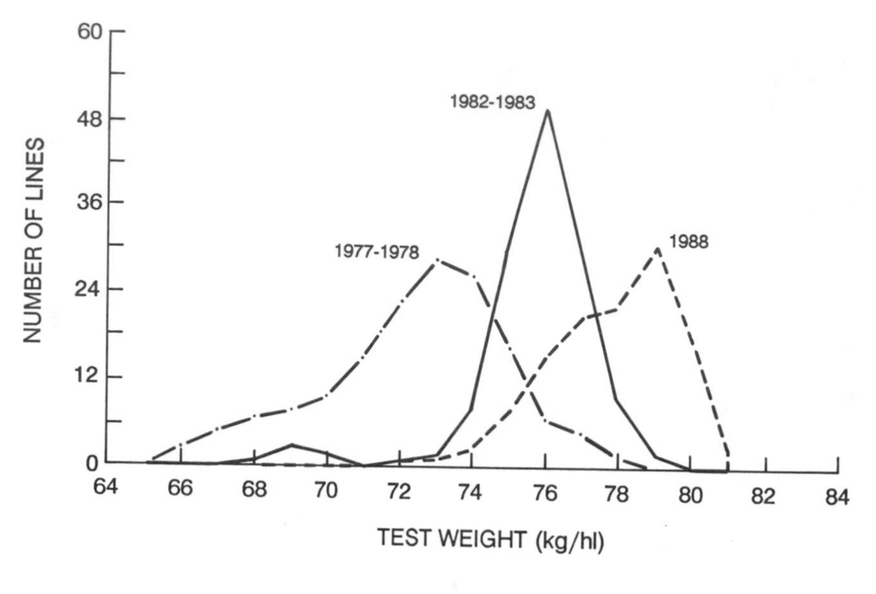

Test Weight (kg/hl)

FIGURE 3.2 Over the last decades, the plumpness of triticale grains has been raised dramatically. This is shown by the enormous increase in test weight between 1978 and 1989. The figure shows the distributions of test weights obtained in Sonora, Mexico, of triticale advanced lines in the tenth, fifteenth, and twentieth International Triticale Screening Nursery. The average test weight for bread wheat is 76 kg per hectoliter. Thus, it can be seen that the most recent triticales have test weights as high or higher than wheat's. (Centro de Investigaciones Agrícolas del Noroeste, Obregón, Mexico)

By and large, triticale grain has less gluten than wheat. However, the differences between varieties are large, and by careful selection CIMMYT researchers have found lines with gluten quality as high as that found in bread wheats.[2] Leavened breads made with these rise to normal levels (see figure 3.1). This is a remarkable discovery, and one that could project triticale instantly into the ranks of top-flight cereals. However, even the best lines cannot yet fully compete with wheat in the most demanding breadmaking uses because of an unusual feature: they form a dough that is more sticky than normal. In small-scale bakeries this is of no concern, but in large modern bakeries with high-speed mixers a small amount (25–30 percent) of wheat flour has to be

[2] Peña and Ballance, 1987.

blended with the triticale before the dough will roll off the mixers in the necessary fashion.[3]

Fertility

The mulelike sterility of this hybrid between two genera seems to have been resolved. In today's advanced triticale lines, the number of seeds in each spike (seedhead) is about the same as in wheat. Normally, more than eight of every ten sites on the spike are filled.

Shriveled Seed

In general, when triticale is grown on fertile sites and under unstressed conditions, researchers no longer consider shriveled seed to be a concern (see figure 3.2). However, when produced on marginal sites, the seeds are sometimes still somewhat shriveled. Soon, even this is likely to improve: lines whose grains remain plump under both good and bad conditions are becoming available.

Grain Yield

Dramatic rises in fertility, grain plumpness, grain size, and field performance have manifested themselves in high yields (see figure 3.3). At sites where conditions are suitable, triticale yields are commonly within wheat's range of 8–9 tons per hectare. On the other hand, at sites where conditions are marginal, the top triticale yields (although much reduced) commonly exceed those of the top wheats by 20–30 percent.

This is true, for instance, in spring triticales.[4] The CIMMYT International Spring Wheat Yield Trials—an annual worldwide test of wheat productivity conducted at some 100 locations throughout the wheat-growing world—now include a triticale variety as a check.[5] Over

---

[3] Some of the world's most productive wheats contain a small amount of rye genes and also have the same problem. Both they and triticale have low mixing tolerance and require mild mixing conditions (see chapter 4).

[4] Agronomically, most cereals come in two main growth habits. The spring types are sown in the spring and harvested, like most crops, in the fall. The winter types are sown in the fall and pass the winter as seedlings, often beneath a blanket of snow.

[5] Variations in climate and environment make the quantity of yield an unreliable measure of relative productivity. A few rows of a standard variety of wheat are therefore placed among the triticale plots. Its yield provides a check against which the triticale yields can be measured.

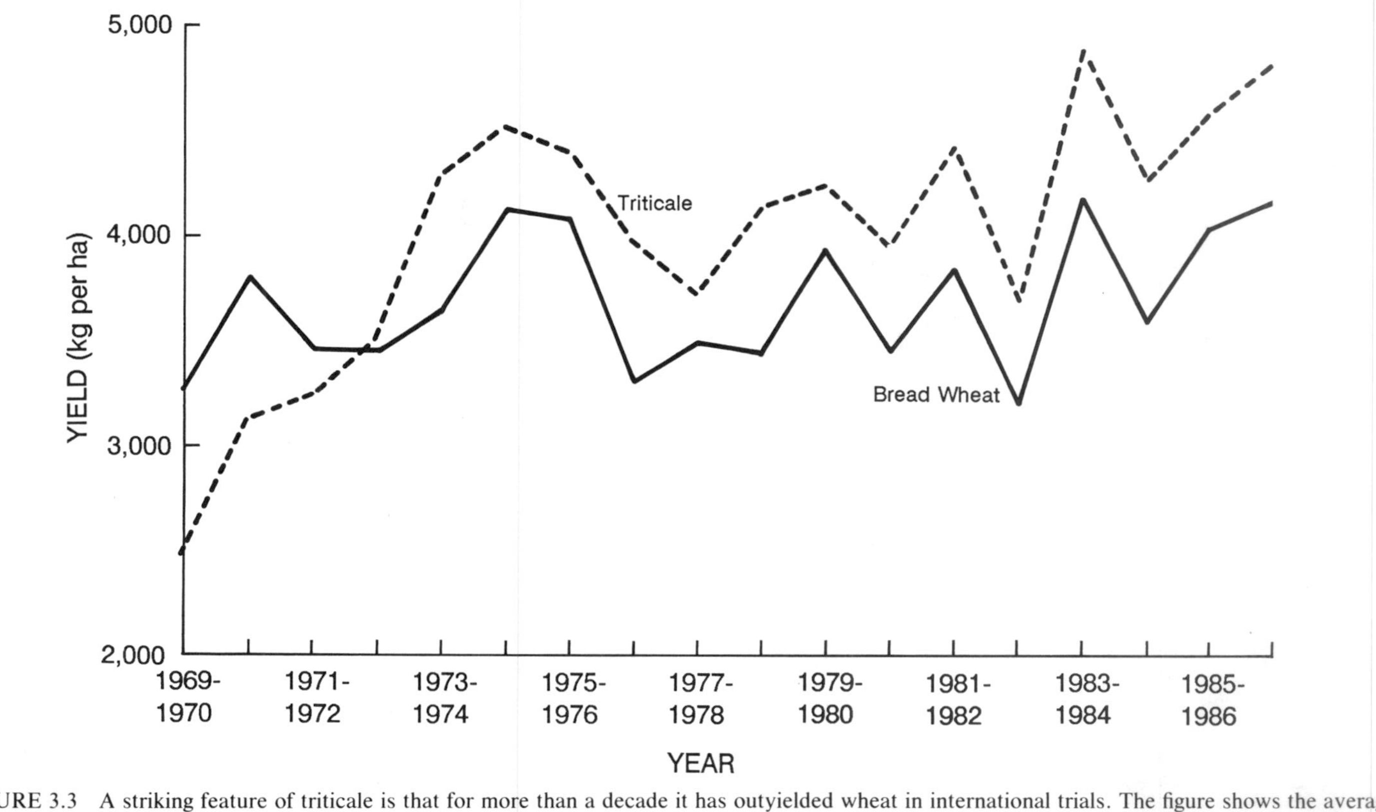

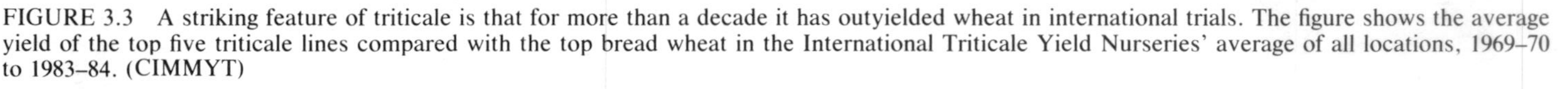
FIGURE 3.3 A striking feature of triticale is that for more than a decade it has outyielded wheat in international trials. The figure shows the average yield of the top five triticale lines compared with the top bread wheat in the International Triticale Yield Nurseries' average of all locations, 1969–70 to 1983–84. (CIMMYT)

the last five years, the triticale has been the highest or second highest yielder out of the 50 wheat varieties tested.

The situation is similar for winter triticales. Lasko, a variety developed in Poland, was included in the International Winter Wheat Performance Nursery in 1983 and 1984. In 1983, it significantly outyielded 28 improved winter wheats from 15 countries at 42 international test sites. In 1984, it significantly outyielded 23 of the winter wheats in the trials and outyielded all the wheats at 47 test sites.

Lodging

Utilizing dwarfing genes from wheat, researchers have rearranged triticale's architecture to make the plants short and rigid enough to overcome lodging. Most lines now withstand adverse wind and weather conditions as well as semidwarf wheats do.

Tillering

Although wheat is still superior, modern triticales have much improved tillering potential. They produce several stems, thereby giving more spikes and potentially greater yields. This is of special importance for helping the plants recover from frost and other damaging conditions that may kill the first spikes to emerge.

Daylength and Lateness

The late maturity that originally contributed to triticale's low yields in Mexico was largely caused by the Canadian triticales' requirements for long daylengths. Current triticales from CIMMYT stocks, however, are daylength neutral and can be grown in many latitudes and, if needed, planted at different times of year.

Eliminating daylength sensitivity has dramatically shortened the maturation time. Selection for rapid dry-down has also helped. As a result, late maturity is now seldom a problem. Since 1983, new lines of early-maturing triticales have been undergoing international testing. A few ripen within five days of CIMMYT's earliest maturing wheats (see figure 3.4).

Disease Resistance

So far, diseases have not seriously limited triticale yields. Except for two cases of stem rust in Australia, diseases have been low. Compared with wheat, triticale seems notably more resistant to leaf blotch, powdery mildew, smuts, bunts, and other fungal infections. However, the crop is not yet planted in sufficient area to trigger serious

FIGURE 3.4 Some triticales now mature at about the same time as the early-maturing bread wheat Sonalika. (CIMMYT)

epidemics, and the Australian experience suggests that the current picture may be misleading for the long run.

One situation in which the plant could become particularly important is where Karnal bunt is a serious problem in wheat. Triticale has displayed remarkable tolerance to this disease, which is now prevalent in the bread wheat crop of northern Mexico and northwestern India, and is a potential threat to the future production of bread wheat in similar climatic regions.

Pest Resistance

Triticales, particularly the complete types (see later), are unattractive to birds because of their tough outer seed husks (glumes) and their long awns (bristles that grow out of glumes).

THE PROMISE OF TRITICALE

The plant's future now seems clear of fundamental agronomic obstacles. A mere three decades after the first practical triticales were made, the crop is ready to forge ahead into production. It has particular promise as a supplement to current foods, feeds, and brewing grains.

FIGURE 3.5 In the state of Michoacan, Mexico, there is a growing commercial trade in triticale for food; thousands of farm families are eating the grain and feeding it to their livestock, currently at a level of 10,000 tons annually. In the city of Pátzcuaro, a major bread company has set up a mill and bakery for producing triticale breads and biscuits. In this area, wheat is unreliable. (A. Morales)

Food

Although most now goes for animal feed, triticale is a tasty grain that in the long run should find its way into many foodstuffs. It has bigger individual seeds than wheat, which for instance, may allow for production of toasted snack foods that are now precluded by small size. In addition, triticale is the second most nutritious grain. Of all the cereals now available for widespread commercial use, only oats have a better nutrient content (see chapter 6).

Triticale is already able to play a big role in making biscuits, cookies, and unleavened breads (for instance, tortillas and chapatis). In the long term, it has more potential for making raised breads than any cereal except wheat. It is a new addition to the world's gluten-containing grains: wheat, rye, and triticale are the only grains that can be used to make raised breads. Other cereals—barley, sorghum, and millets, for example—lack the qualities necessary for making leavened breads. As already noted, some CIMMYT triticales have gluten quality as good as that found in bread wheat. Breads made with these triticales are indistinguishable from wheat breads in texture, appearance, and loaf volume. However, as previously noted, they require slower mixing and are not suited to the high-speed mixers used in large industrial bakeries.

FIGURE 3.6 Triticale's strength as a crop is its ability to thrive on many sites where wheat and other cereals grow poorly. . . .

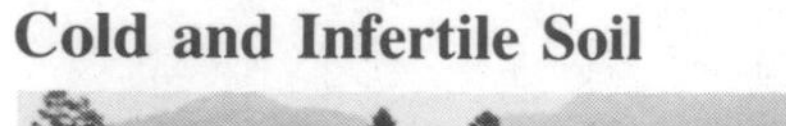

Cold and Infertile Soil

Pátzcuaro, Mexico. Triticale (left) performs better than wheat in this upland location. (CIMMYT)

Sand

Huamantla, central Mexico. In extremely sandy soil, wheat (right) fails, whereas triticale (left) succeeds. (G. Varughese)

Boron-Toxic Soil

Two Wells, South Australia. Triticale thrives in soil with high levels of boron. Wheat grows poorly in this area because of the occurrence of up to 100 ppm boron. (K.V. Cooper)

Disease

Gisenyi, Rwanda. Stunted wheat (foreground) grossly infested with stripe rust while triticale (background) is clean. (F. Zillinsky)

Salt

Yaqui Valley, Mexico. Safflower (left) stressed to the point of death by salty soil while the thick stand of triticale (right) is growing well. (F. Zillinsky)

Acid

Highlands of Ecuador. Barley (foreground) fails on this acid site, while triticale (background) is unaffected. (H. Vivar, CIMMYT)

Manganese-Deficient Soil

Two Wells, South Australia. Triticale on calcareous sand deficient in manganese. Wheat and barley barely survive on this site. (K.V. Cooper)

Drought

Kathmandu, Nepal. Wheat (foreground) has died for lack of water while triticale (background) is still green and productive. (F. Zillinsky)

MARGINAL LANDS

Triticale is a potentially important addition to the global armory of weapons for combating hunger as world populations rise. It seems likely to play a role in sparing millions of the poor from the ravages of malnutrition in Africa, Asia, and Latin America. Its greatest promise is probably for producing flat breads in locations where wheat growing is unreliable. Given the right temperature and moisture conditions, it can grow in the same range of soils as wheat. However, on certain problem soils it performs better than wheat. Examples of such soils follow.

Dry and Sandy Soils

Under drought conditions, triticale's biomass production falls, but wheat's normally falls much further, and triticale's relative advantage becomes pronounced. In the savanna region of central Brazil, for example, triticale's biomass is frequently twice that of wheat. At CIMMYT's dryland site at Huamantla, Mexico (250–400 mm annual rainfall), triticales have consistently outperformed wheats in biomass production for more than a decade, and several dairymen in the area have switched to growing it for feeding their cows.

Acid Soils

The occurrence of acid soils is one of the most serious and widespread problems in both the lowland and highland tropics. Acidity binds up phosphorus and a few minor elements. When this happens, plants can't absorb enough of these necessary nutrients and they grow poorly, if at all. Acidity also frees up other minerals, notably aluminum, that are toxic: once absorbed these damage or kill the roots, and the crop dies.

Triticales show high yields in acid soils (with high soluble aluminum) such as oxisols and ultisols and on phosphorus-binding soils such as andosols. On acid soils, the crop's potential is unmatched by wheat. This remarkable quality has been demonstrated in Poland, Kenya, Ethiopia, India, Ecuador, Brazil, Mexico, and elsewhere. In each case, various triticales outyielded wheat. (See, for example, figure 3.6.) Generally, they had 20–30 percent higher yields than the wheats they were tested against. This is especially important where soils cannot be deacidified because of cost, remoteness, or lack of lime (see chapter 8).

Many countries—Brazil and Zambia, for instance—have huge areas of acid soils where triticale might be particularly valuable. Some also import large amounts of wheat and might benefit greatly from a locally grown bread grain.

Although breeders are creating aluminum-tolerant bread wheats, they have not, so far, been able to match triticale's levels of tolerance. In one Brazilian trial, for instance, 10 of the most aluminum-tolerant wheats were compared against 10 triticales. The top 10 yields were all triticales; the lowest triticale yielded more than the highest wheat.[6] Moreover, because nothing special has been done to select for aluminum tolerance in triticale, even greater potential could be inherent in the plant.

Alkaline Soils

Triticale also seems promising for alkaline soils. Preliminary findings from Mexico, Spain, Portugal, and the United States indicate that its seedlings perform better than those of other small-grain crops on highly alkaline and calcareous soils.[7] In the United States, a variety called "Flora" has been released specifically for use on alkaline soils in Oregon. It is a winter habit variety—a little late maturing and with grains that are shriveled—yet it yields as well as wheat on good soils and much better than wheat on high pH soils.[8]

Mineral-Deficient and High-Boron Soils

It has been observed in Australia that triticale appears exceptionally tolerant of soils deficient in copper, manganese, or zinc.[9] Increasingly, deficiencies in these elements are recognized as widespread limitations to crop yields. Zinc deficiency, for example, occurs on many heavy black soils (such as the ustolls and borolls and montmorillonitic soils, which are found worldwide).

Also in Australia, triticale appears to be growing better than wheat in high-boron soils. This is an important early observation because boron is toxic to most crops, and its effects are now recognized as a problem in many low-rainfall areas with alkaline soils.[10]

---

[6] In Brazil and other areas where legumes are grown, liming is usually practiced to raise soil pH, but even on limed soils, triticale has demonstrated a yield advantage over wheat. Information from A. Baier. Similar evidence has been gained in laboratory screening tests conducted at CIMMYT. Information from E. Villegas.

[7] Information from CIMMYT.

[8] Information from R. Metzger and M. Kolding.

[9] Information from D. R. Marshall.

[10] Information from D. R. Marshall.

4
Limitations and Uncertainties

The greatest service which can be rendered any country is to add a useful plant to its culture; especially, a bread grain. . . .

THOMAS JEFFERSON, 1821

END USES

In solving triticale's basic agronomic problems, CIMMYT has contributed greatly to the creation of this promising new crop. Overcoming the shriveled seed was particularly important as far as the crop's end uses are concerned. For example, it improved the milling yield and gluten content. Unfortunately, however, it produced grains that result in a dough so sticky that it won't roll out of high-speed mixers. For industrial bakeries turning out perhaps 50,000 loaves an hour, that is clearly unacceptable.

What will finally make triticale a major resource is the improvement of the end-use products—particularly leavened breads made in large-scale bakeries. A plant combining triticale's field qualities with all of bread wheat's baking qualities would sweep rapidly into massive use around the world.

As noted previously, triticale can already be used in many products without sacrificing quality. For making chapatis or tortillas and other flat breads, it is already commercially viable. For small-scale bakeries, the sticky dough is also of little consequence, and triticale is even now appropriate for widespread use in making raised breads on all but the largest scale.

However, the fact that leavened breads cannot be made in industrial quantities casts a shadow over the whole crop. For one thing, triticale grain faces difficulties as an export to industrialized nations that plan to use it as a bread grain. For another, the biggest single grain buyers—even in poor countries—are often large city bakeries. For their high-speed equipment they need grain without the sticky-dough problem.

If nations are to avoid two-tier marketing and if triticale is to shed the stigma of inferiority, the crop should be suitable for even the most challenging bread baking processes.

Functional Properties

Although recent triticale varieties in Mexico have demonstrated greatly improved milling and baking qualities, triticale grain, by and large, has a slightly lower flour yield (milling rate) than wheat. This is especially true if it was produced under conditions that promote shriveled kernels.

GENE BASE

In producing spring triticales, the variety Armadillo was a breakthrough. It brought fertility, high yields, and plump seeds at a time when these seemed impossible to achieve. But it was also a bane. Although, the high fertility found in Armadillo led to many of today's successes in spring triticales, it also created a genetic vulnerability. In passing through Armadillo, CIMMYT had to sacrifice the breadth of environmental tolerance that would have come if several "Armadillos" had been found. Also, in its earliest stages, the small CIMMYT research program had to make its triticales from wheats developed for irrigated agriculture. These had less than average tolerance for adversity.

The result of these genetic bottlenecks is that today's triticales have a fairly narrow germplasm base. The crop already has shown remarkable adaptability, but when additional genetic diversity is available, its resilience could become even more remarkable.

PRODUCTION PROBLEMS

Agronomically, triticale is similar to wheat. The two crops are subject to the same stresses and limitations, and their cultivation and management are usually handled in the same way. Triticale, therefore, has the major advantage in that it requires no new technology or methods.

However, triticale is not wheat, and—depending on the varieties used and the local climatic and soil conditions—slight modifications are needed. Thus, one cannot assume that the new crop's requirements are identical to those of wheat. Triticale agronomy has to be "fine-tuned" in each area where it is to be grown.

Also, in certain locations various triticale lines may show unexpected agronomic problems. Highlighted below are some specific concerns over the currently available lines. For each concern, modern breeding has obtained fairly good lines; the problem remains to combine them into several varieties. (It should be recognized, of course, that even in wheat no faultless variety exists.)

Lodging

"Top-heaviness" or weak straw can still be a problem in well-watered, highly productive areas where the plants grow overly tall and lush. However, triticale is most likely to be employed in marginal environments where lodging is seldom a problem. Short, highly promising lines are now under evaluation so that soon, even under good environmental conditions, lodging should not be a problem.

Slow Ripening

The long grain-filling period of the current cultivars makes the crop more susceptible to stresses. In environments where there is drought or excessive heat during and after flowering, the grain can fill out poorly and end up shriveled. This is also true for wheat, but triticale is more susceptible because present lines take longer to mature their grains. This problem, too, is likely to soon pass. Early-maturing types are already in advanced stages of development (see figure 3.4).

Threshing

Triticale harvests easily and threshes well, and seed shattering is not a problem. However, a few types—notably, some European winter varieties and some of the completes (all rye chromosomes present, see chapter 5)—are hard to thresh. Some of these recalcitrant types have glumes that clasp the grain too tightly; others have soft grains that can break during threshing. (Harder types are now becoming available, however.)

Dormancy and Sprouting

There are large differences in dormancy between triticale varieties: winter triticales have dormancy; spring triticales from CIMMYT currently have little or none. The types with dormancy require a "rest period" before they will germinate. The types without dormancy germinate readily, sometimes so readily that if the weather is damp at harvest time, they may begin sprouting even before being harvested from the parent plant. Although new lines are greatly improved, preharvest sprouting is still a problem with most CIMMYT triticales. It does not occur everywhere, nor with every line, but in those sites where moist conditions prevail during harvest (for example, in parts of Mexico, Brazil, Canada, and northern Europe), sprouting can limit the quality of current CIMMYT varieties.

Diseases

Like other crops, triticale is susceptible to some diseases, and local adaptation is needed to overcome this. As noted, most triticale diseases are not devastating. However, it is too soon to tell what the effects will be if the crop is grown on large areas and resistances break down. This has already happened in Australia where previously resistant varieties suddenly and unexpectedly succumbed to stem rust.

In general, the most serious threats are leaf rust, stem rust, stripe rust, scab, eye-spot, spot blotch, and bacterial diseases. Leaf rust reduces yield but does not kill the plant. The others, however, are potentially devastating. In the long run, most diseases can probably be overcome by incorporating genes from resistant strains of wheat or rye. Resistance to rust diseases can almost certainly be incorporated this way, but even in wheat, resistance to scab and spot blotch is limited, and finding ways to overcome them will be more complicated. It is not impossible, however, because triticale's rye genome brings all the cultivated and wild ryes within reach for transferring resistance to triticale. Also, cytogenetic methods have been developed—and molecular biological techniques are in the making—that permit transfer of resistance genes from even more genetically distant wild relatives.

Ergot, a worrisome disease of rye, also affects triticale. This fungal infection spreads from wild grasses and can be a problem in temperate regions. However, ergot infects empty florets, and in triticale the improvement in floral fertility has dramatically reduced its incidence. In most areas (outside high latitudes—such as Canada), ergot in triticale has now decreased to levels comparable to the low levels of wheat.

Genetic Reproductive Stability

Because it is so new and because it is a combination of divergent species, today's triticales are prone to genetic instability. Occasional missing chromosomes produce plants with poor seed, poorly filled spikes, and sometimes even sterility. If the seeds of any triticale crop are repeatedly resown over several generations, an accumulation of chromosomal instability may lead to an increase of sterility, a decline in grain yield, and a rise in highly unstable types.[1]

Postharvest Handling

The kernels of most triticales are softer than those of hard wheats, and are therefore slightly more subject to insect damage. This, in general, makes them slightly more difficult to store. However, plant breeders are increasing the kernel hardness, and the problem should soon disappear.

LACK OF RECOGNITION

In the marketplace, triticale faces a general lack of appreciation. The plant's agricultural and dietary niches are not established in many places thus far, and few countries have established pricing structures or grain standards for triticale. This can be a considerable handicap for a newcomer confronting well-established, centuries-old systems of marketing and processing, all based on the characteristics and uses of other grains.

Anywhere that triticale is to be produced on a commercial scale it needs a clear set of procedures for marketing, transporting, handling, and grading the grain. Farmers can then adjust their planting and marketing plans accordingly.

If triticale brings a lower price than competing crops—as seems likely, given its newness—it will have to present yield or other advantages to compensate. There is ample evidence that it can do this, particularly in marginal areas where it is likely to outperform wheat by a profitable margin. If it is for use in animal feeds, it must also outperform barley, sorghum, oats, or other competing grains.[2]

[1] Marshall and Ellison, 1986.

[2] A wide variety of uses are reviewed by Skovmand et al., 1984, and by Wu et al., 1978.

5
Breeding Triticale

Plant breeding is a long, repetitious undertaking demanding infinite patience and promising no certain success. Success, if attained, is rarely dramatic and often illusory.

B. S. DODGE
It Started in Eden

Plants in different genera are normally separated by strong barriers of infertility: they will not crossbreed because the pollen of one is incompatible with the ovum of the other. This natural barrier makes triticale difficult to create. In nature, the necessary cross-pollination occurs infrequently and is successful only when rye is the male parent.

WHEAT

Wheat itself evolved through natural hybridization. It, too, is a composite of different species. The various cultivated wheats are of three main types, each genetically distinct and characterized by different numbers of chromosomes.

Diploid wheat. The most primitive cultivated wheat is a grass called "einkorn" (*Triticum monococcum*).[1] This is a diploid[2] species and is still cultivated in parts of Turkey and the southern Soviet Union.

Tetraploid wheat. Thousands of years ago, before the dawn of civilization, einkorn hybridized with another diploid wild grass. (The actual species is not known for certain, but it was probably similar to the wild goat grass *Aegilops speltoides*, also called *Triticum speltoides*.) Chance chromosomal doubling resulted in tetraploid wheats. At first, these held their grains tightly, but after they were taken into cultivation, mutants appeared that had "naked" grains that could be easily threshed out. For at least 7,000 years, farmers have selected, planted, nurtured,

[1] It is a domesticated form of the wild grass *Triticum boeoticum*.
[2] *Ploidy*, in recent usage, means *-fold*. It is used to refer to the number of sets of chromosomes a particular plant (or animal) has. Thus, diploid refers to organisms whose cells have twofold sets; tetraploid, fourfold; hexaploid, sixfold; and octoploid, eightfold. In wheat, rye, and triticale, each set contains seven chromosomes, so that diploids have 14 chromosomes; tetraploids, 28 chromosomes; hexaploids, 42 chromosomes; and octoploids, 56 chromosomes.

and replanted the seeds of these scrawny grasses, gradually transforming them into plump, productive, modern wheats. Among their creations is durum wheat (*Triticum turgidum* var. *durum*), one of the two wheats that today feed much of the world.

Hexaploid wheat. Subsequently, the tetraploid wheats hybridized with yet another wild, weedy goat grass (called either *Aegilops squarrosa* or *Triticum tauschii*). Again chromosome doubling occurred, resulting in hexaploid wheat. After thousands of years of nurturing, it, too, was transformed into a valuable crop—bread wheat, or common wheat (*Triticum aestivum*). It has become the world's most widely grown breadmaking crop.[3]

Chromosome Designations

As a shorthand designation, geneticists use letters to indicate the chromosome sets contributed by each wheat ancestor. The chromosome set of einkorn is designated A; the chromosome set from the species that resembles *Aegilops speltoides* is designated B; and the chromosome set from *Aegilops squarrosa* is designated D.

With this nomenclature, the series of steps leading to the genomes in today's wheats becomes clearer. When einkorn (AA) hybridized with the species resembling *Aegilops speltoides* (BB), it gave rise to the tetraploid durum wheats, whose chromosome composition is designated AABB. When one of these tetraploids, in turn, hybridized with *Aegilops squarrosa* (DD), it gave rise to the hexaploid wheats AABBDD. The D set markedly contributes to the strong gluten that makes these "bread wheats."

Creating Triticales

Triticale is merely a recent extension of the prehistoric hybridization process that led to modern wheat: the rye set is simply added to wheat.

To create triticale, the chosen wheat plant is emasculated—in other words, its immature male reproductive organs (anthers) are removed so that self-fertilization cannot occur. At flowering time, fresh pollen from the chosen rye plant is transferred to the chosen wheat's female reproductive organs (stigmas).

The fertilized cells (embryos) produced from this cross-fertilization carry a single set of chromosomes from both parents. Rye, a diploid, has two sets of chromosomes, designated R. If breadwheat (AABBDD)

[3] The combinations of species that make up the different wheats are actually more complicated than described here. For more information, readers are referred to Morris and Sears, 1987.

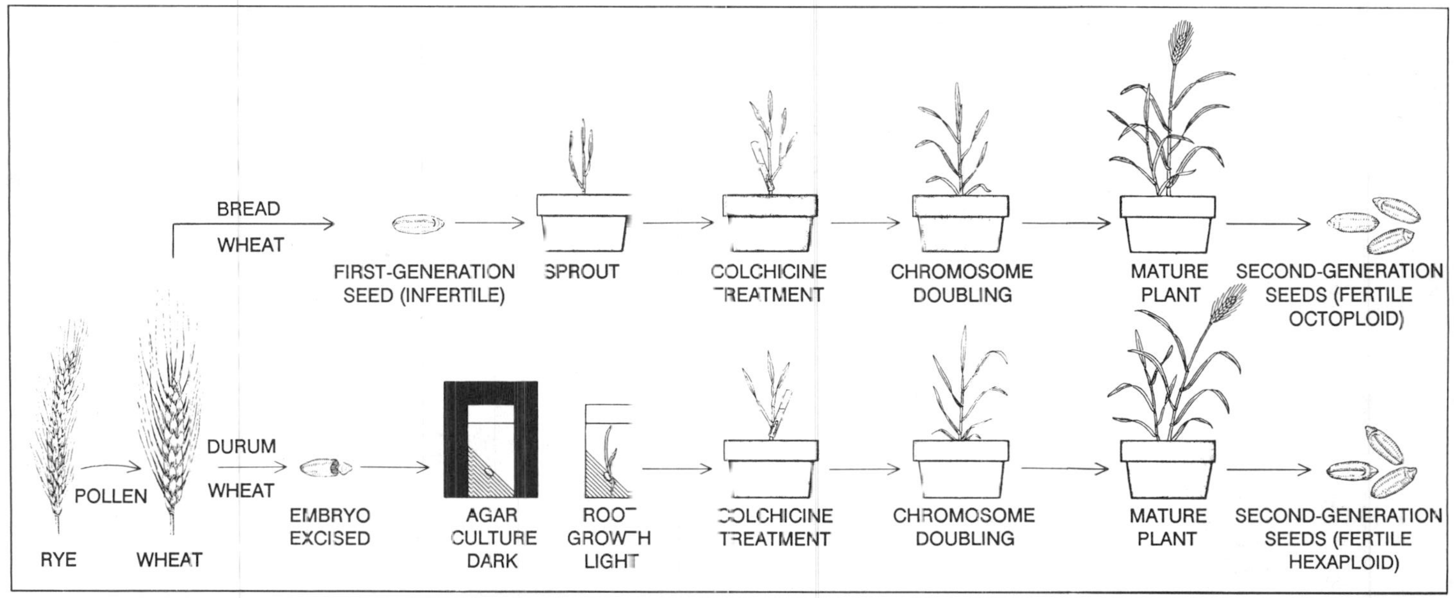

FIGURE 5.1 First-generation triticale seeds are usually sterile even though they may germinate. The sequence at top shows the system of crossing bread wheats with rye. In this case, the sterility is overcome by treating seedlings with the alkaloid colchicine. Applied to the tip of a growing sprout, this substance interferes with mitotic division in the fast-reproducing cells in such a manner that the number of chromosomes is doubled. The doubled chromosome complement gives rise to fertile flowers that later grow on the stem. The seeds produced by these flowers are also usually fertile. This pathway yields octoploid triticales. The sequence at bottom shows the system used in crossing durum wheats with rye. This produces seeds that will not germinate, and embryo culture is used to produce first-generation seedlings. The technique consists in excising the embryo from seeds that are immature (14-20 days after fertilization) and culturing the embryo in an agar medium. The culture is kept in the dark until the embryo sprouts and then is kept in constant illumination. Later the sprout is transplanted to a peat pot and treated with colchicine as above. This pathway yields hexaploid triticales.

is pollinated with rye (RR) it produces a hybrid with a chromosome formula designated ABDR. This is the sterile type of haploid hybrid that A.S. Wilson produced in 1876.

To make a seed-producing triticale, the haploid seedling is treated with a weak solution of colchicine. This is usually fed to the plant through the roots, and it migrates to the crown area of the growing shoot. In the apical growing regions where cell division is occurring, colchicine suppresses the orderly separation of chromosomes during cell division. Instead of pulling away from each other, the products of cell division (the sister chromatids) usually remain side by side. The cell wall that normally would grow between them does not form. The resulting nucleus therefore retains both sets of chromosomes. Instead of being ABDR, it doubles into an octoploid triticale, AABBDDRR. Every chromosome now has a partner and normal reduction division can proceed when the time comes for germ-cell formation.

If durum wheat (AABB) is simply pollinated with rye (RR), mature hybrid seeds (haploid, ABR) are almost never produced. However, the pollen does fertilize some of the ova, and the resulting embryos begin growing—only to abort approximately 15 days later because of endosperm incompatibility. However, these embryos can be excised and maintained artificially in a sterile culture medium. The culture medium provides them with nutrients, and they grow into plantlets with roots and leaves. They are still sterile, but when treated with colchicine, as described above, these plantlets produce partially fertile hexaploid triticales (AABBRR).

Hexaploid Triticales

Almost all work worldwide centers on hexaploid triticales. The main reason is that they have better vigor and reproductive stability than the octoploids currently available. Also, in general they show better disease resistance and selection response. However, as they are made by crossing durum wheat (AABB) with rye (RR), they lack the bread wheat D chromosomes that should contribute the best breadmaking qualities.

Octoploid Triticales

Octoploid triticales, as noted, result when bread wheat is employed in the cross. Because they contain the D-genome chromosomes of bread wheat, they normally have good breadmaking qualities. However, at present, they tend to be unstable and unpredictable in the field, and currently are used only in the People's Republic of China. Nonetheless, some of the most valuable genetic traits are found in octoploids, and the creation of practical octoploid triticales is an important promise for the future.

So far, octoploids have been most valuable for improving hexaploid triticales. At CIMMYT in the 1970s, the crop's agronomic breakthroughs came from crosses between Armadillo (a hexaploid) and some newly created octoploid triticales, of which the Maya group were among the first. The variety Mapache was selected from the cross between Armadillo and Maya 2. It was released for commercial production in Mexico under the name "Cananea 79." Its performance in international trials was outstanding. In 38 locations it outyielded wheat. Today, almost half of the spring hexaploid varieties released worldwide are derived from it either directly or indirectly.[4]

Primary Triticales

The products that arise directly from crossing wheat with rye (followed by chromosome doubling) are collectively called primary triticales. They are pure triticales, unmodified by further hybridization. To differing degrees, they share problems of partial sterility, shriveled seed, low yield, and poor agronomic type. But they are pure lines—homozygous as a result of chromosome doubling for all gene pairs and so they are stable. Like a standard crop variety, they remain much the same year after year. (They are, however, a little more unstable than normal varieties of wheat.)

Secondary Triticales

Plant breeders, on discovering that primary triticales were not agronomically useful, began to hybridize these triticales with other primary types and with wheat, or even some other species. From such crosses arose an array of triticale types that are generally called "secondary triticales" because they have new combinations of wheat and/or rye chromosomes. Except for some successful octoploid primary triticales developed and used in China, secondary triticales form the basis of the world's triticale industry at this time.

Complete and Substituted Triticales

Among CIMMYT's spring triticales there are two major types: "completes" and "substitutes."

Complete triticales retain unchanged all the chromosomes of the rye parent. Many of the most resilient triticale varieties are of this type. Completes tend to be more productive under stressful conditions. They

[4] Information from F. Zillinsky.

TABLE 5.1 Important CIMMYT Advanced Lines of Hexaploid Triticale Available in 1987.

Name	Type[a]	Qualities
Armadillo	S	Highly fertile, daylength-insensitive, one-gene dwarf.
Yoreme 75	S	First line released. Good plant type, good productivity.
Cananea 79	S	First triticale in international nurseries with wide adaptability and high yield potential.
Panda	S	First triticale with good test weight (over 75 kg/hl).
Beagle	C	First complete with high adaptability and yield. Released in Portugal, Australia, USA, and Canada.
Juanillo	C	Most productive spring triticale in international trials since 1980. Most widely adapted spring triticale. Released in many countries under different names.
Juan	C	Derived from Juanillo. Developed in California.
Currency	C	One of CIMMYT's first dwarf completes. Main cultivar used in Australia.
Gnu, Stier	C	Dwarfs with high yield and adaptation. Have 6D/6A substitution.
Rhino	C	High-yielding line with stable test weight.
Tatu	C	Best complete triticale for breadmaking.
Civet	C	One of the most drought-tolerant varieties.
Ardilla	C	First early-maturing complete triticale. Comparable to earliest substituted triticales and bread wheats. Has 6D/6A substitution.

[a] C = complete R genome present
S = wheat chromosome 2D substituted for chromosome 2R

All CIMMYT triticales are of the spring type.

SOURCE: G. Varughese and T. Barker.

retain much of rye's inherent robustness, and they tend to thrive under various difficult conditions, including sandy soils, high elevations, and high rainfall. Thus, they appear to be the triticales of choice for marginal environments.

Two of CIMMYT's complete triticales, Beagle and Drira, are progenitors of many of the present-day commercial spring triticales used in Australia, Spain, and various Third World countries. In addition to CIMMYT lines, other completes, such as the winter triticale Lasko, are being used in Europe (see chapter 7).

Substituted triticales, in CIMMYT's terminology, are those in which rye chromosome 2R has been replaced by chromosome 2D of bread wheat. The discovery of this chromosome repatterning was an important event in the history of triticale. It began with Armadillo, which has this trait.

Under nonstressed conditions, the 2D for 2R (2D/2R) substituted types perform better than the completes. They tend to mature earlier and may be better for breadmaking. Like the completes, several of

TABLE 5.2 Promising Non-CIMMYT Advanced Lines of Hexaploid Triticale Available in 1987.

Origin	Name	Type[a]	Qualities
Poland	Lasko	C	Very productive winter type, resistant to cold and disease. Requires plant-growth regulator.
	Salvo	C	
Hungary	Bokolo	C	Promising, dwarf winter type, bred for wheat soils. Widely grown in Eastern Europe and France.
France	Clercal		
	Raboliot		
Spain	Triticor		
Canada	Carman	C	
	Wintri	C	One of the most winter hardy.
	Decade		
	T44		Spring type, high yielding.
United States	6TABi		
	Marvel		
	Siskiyou	C	

[a] C = complete set of chromosomes present

the substituted types appear to maintain a high lysine content. And improvements in dough strength and breadmaking quality are considered less difficult to achieve in the substituted than in the complete type. (Whether this is due to the presence of chromosome 2D or to the loss of chromosome 2R is uncertain.) Of 42 commercial triticale cultivars for which the chromosome constitution is known, 16 are completes and 26 are substitutes carrying the 2D/2R substitution.

In addition, about 20 percent of CIMMYT lines and some European winter lines have a 6D/6A substitution. In these triticales, the rye genome is intact, and chromosomes from the D-genome of wheat have replaced those from either the A or B-genomes, also of wheat. This allows for both D-genome and R-genome chromosomes to be present in hexaploid triticale, thus combining the best qualities of both parents—the breadmaking qualities of wheat and the robustness of the rye plant.

Chromosome substitution raises the possibility of a far-reaching reorganization of the chromosomal and genomic composition. Researchers can make many different wheat-like triticales with various combinations of two or more substituted wheat chromosomes, or even triticale-like wheats with one or a few rye chromosomes.[5] This can be of benefit to breeders of all three crops: wheat, rye, and triticale (see chapter 8).

[5] Indeed, some of this decade's most exciting bread wheat varieties—including Veery 'S'—contain part of a single rye chromosome (1R) to which much of the yield advantage has been attributed. These, like triticale, suffer from the "sticky dough" syndrome.

6
Food and Feed Uses

As populations explode and come to demand more and better food, man's inescapable reliance on food plants has made the production of new, hardier, and better kinds of crop plants almost the only way left to fight man's ancient and universal enemy—hunger.

B. S. DODGE
It Started in Eden

Triticale, like red wheat, has a brownish seed coat. It gives an off-white flour, much like the whole-wheat flours that come from red wheats. However, the plant breeding department at Punjab Agricultural University in Ludhiana, India, has recently produced white-seeded types.[1] Thus, although much more research is needed, white-seeded triticales are soon likely to be available for those places where markets overwhelmingly demand white flour.

NUTRITIONAL VALUE

Compared with wheat, triticale has slightly higher levels of most of the nutritious constituents. However, whether this will be meaningful in the long run is uncertain because the levels of all constituents are extremely variable—reflecting both triticale's mixed parentage and its youthfulness as a crop. Nonetheless, the main nutritional qualities of the current types are given below.

Protein

Early triticale lines varied enormously in protein content but generally were very high. For example, in the early 1970s, protein contents were mainly in the range of 15 to 18 percent of the total grain weight.[2]

[1] Gill, 1986.
[2] Hulse and Laing, 1974.

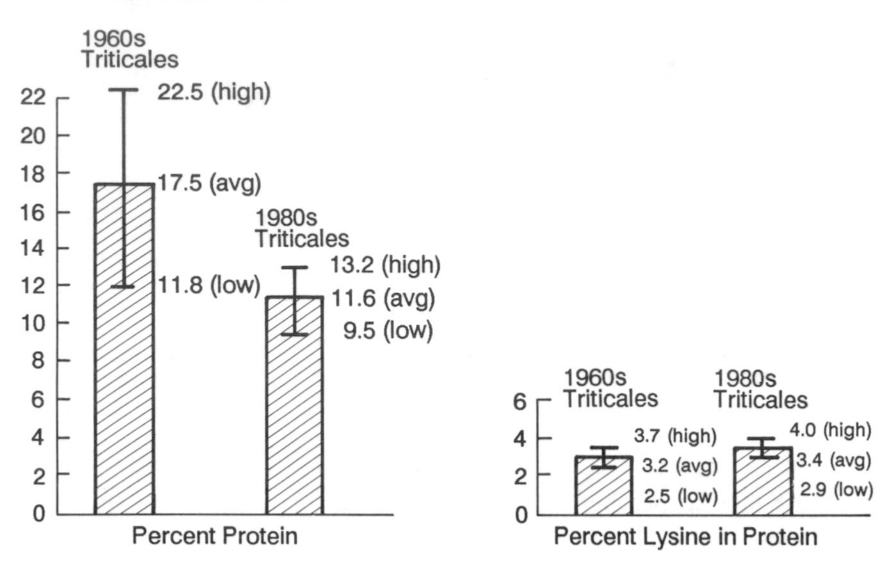

FIGURE 6.1 Protein and lysine contents. Early triticales were characterized by high levels of protein, averaging more than 17 percent. However, these had grains that were shriveled and unacceptable in the marketplace. Over the years, as the kernel characteristics (especially the ratio of endosperm to bran) have improved, the average protein content has drastically declined. Today, it is at near normal levels for a cereal. Nonetheless, the high level of lysine has remained. Few wheats are in triticale's range of 3.7–4.0 percent lysine. Most are around 2.7 percent. In lysine content, therefore, triticale is exceptional for a cereal. (E. Villegas, CIMMYT)

Wheat, by comparison, has an average protein content of only 12.9 percent. This demonstration of triticale's apparent nutritional superiority led to much publicity and to claims of it being a "super food."

However, this was misleading. The protein levels were high only because in the shriveled seeds of that time starch deposition was unnaturally low. The underdeveloped endosperm meant that the proportion of bran and germ (high protein) was greater than is normal in a cereal grain. As subsequent breeding and selection for plump seeds increased the size of the endosperm, the proportion of germ and bran decreased. This led to an inevitable decrease in the proportion of protein and an increase in the proportion of starch to near normal levels.

Although it might seem that reducing the protein content in the grain was a retrograde step, the loss has been more than offset by the increase in overall crop yield. Thus, in 1968 (when protein contents averaged 17.5 percent and the best yields were 2,500 kg per hectare), triticale produced 425 kg protein per hectare. By 1973 (when the protein content had dropped to 13.7 percent, but the best yields were

TABLE 6.1 Amino Acid Content.

Amino Acid	Triticale (Yoreme)	Wheat (INIA) g/100 g of protein	Rye (Snoopy)
Lysine	3.44	2.83	4.02
Threonine	3.55	2.98	4.06
Methionine[a]	1.28	1.42	1.35
Isoleucine	3.45	2.68	3.70
Leucine	7.20	7.22	7.75
Phenylalanine	4.94	3.77	4.74
Valine	4.48	3.73	5.10
Tryptophan	1.02	1.10	ND

[a] Partial destruction during hydrolysis

SOURCE: General Laboratories, CIMMYT, 1982.

up to 8,000 kg per hectare), it was producing 1,100 kg protein per hectare.[3]

Protein Quality

A protein's biological quality is determined by its proportions of various essential amino acids. These are the building blocks of protein that cannot be synthesized by humans (and other nonruminants such as pigs and poultry) and must therefore be obtained entirely from food. In triticale, as in most cereal grains, the "first limiting" amino acid is lysine.

Although lysine is the amino acid most lacking in triticale, it is present in higher proportions than in commercial wheats. Of 5,500 triticale lines analyzed by CIMMYT in 1974, the protein averaged 3.4 percent lysine. In commercial wheat, by comparison, the total protein fraction averages about 2.8 percent of lysine. Therefore, triticale protein is almost 25 percent richer in lysine than wheat protein is (see table 6.1).[4]

In triticale protein, the content of threonine—another essential amino acid—is approximately 10 percent higher than that in wheat protein. Beyond lysine and threonine, there seem to be no significant differences between the amino acids of triticale and wheat.

[3] Recently, wild wheats (tetraploids) with protein percentage of up to 30 percent have been discovered in Israel. Thus, it appears that productive commercial wheats with up to 20 percent protein will soon be available. There should be no difficulty in transferring the genes for high protein to triticale from the high-protein durum wheats under development. Information from E. Sears.

[4] Villegas et al., 1980. More recent analyses in California have found the difference in lysine content between triticale and wheat to be in the same range (approximately 30 percent). Information from C. Qualset.

TABLE 6.2 Vitamin Content.[a]

	Triticale (Winter type[b]) µg/g	Triticale (Spring type[c]) µg/g	Wheat[d] µg/g	Rye[e] µg/g
Thiamine	9.8	9.0	9.9	7.7
Riboflavin	2.5	2.5	3.1	2.9
Niacin	17.9	16.0	48.3	15.3
Biotin	0.06	0.07	0.06	0.05
Folacin	0.56	0.77	0.56	0.49
Pantothenic Acid	9.1	8.3	9.1	6.3
Vitamin B_6	4.7	4.9	4.7	3.4

[a] Dry basis
[b] TR 383
[c] 6TA204
[d] Chris
[e] Prolific

SOURCE: Michela and Lorenz, 1976.

Other Nutrients

In triticale, the major minerals, such as potassium and phosphorus, generally have marginally higher levels than in wheat;[5] the micro-nutrient elements, such as sodium, manganese, iron, and zinc, are also a little higher.

On the other hand, triticale's vitamin content is about the same as that of wheat.[6] Triticale's most limiting vitamin is niacin (see table 6.2).

The level of digestible energy is also the same in both triticale and wheat: triticale contains 14.1 MJ per kg; wheat, 14.4 MJ per kg.

Nutritional Performance

In general, trials on living animals have shown triticale to have a biological value 15–20 percent higher than wheat's (see table 6.3). This is important because biological value measures the proportion of absorbed nitrogen that is retained by the body. The superiority is probably due to triticale's higher content of lysine and threonine.

True protein digestibility—the proportion of food nitrogen that is absorbed by the bloodstream—is above 90 percent in triticale protein, a figure comparable to that of wheat protein and much higher than that of rye protein.[7]

True digestibilities of individual amino acids in wheat, triticale, and rye have been compared in studies with pigs. The lysine availability in triticale (81 percent) is higher than that in wheat and other cereals.

[5] Lorenz et al., 1974.
[6] Michela and Lorenz, 1976.
[7] Taverner, 1986.

TABLE 6.3 Percent of True Protein Digestibility, Biological Value, and Net Protein Utilization of Some Varieties of Triticale Compared with a Wheat Variety, Using Male White Rats.

	Triticale			Wheat
	Mapache	Beagle	PC-297	Hermosillo-77
True Protein Digestibility	92.7	91.0	91.5	92.0
Biological Value	66.1	69.9	59.3	57.6
Net Protein Utilization	61.3	63.7	54.2	52.9

SOURCE: Villegas et al., 1980.

In triticale, the digestibility of gross energy is also high (87 percent), fully comparable to the corresponding values in wheat and maize.[8]

Antinutritional Factors

Many early trials in which triticale was fed to animals produced responses inconsistent with expectations based on the grain's composition. Apparently, the discrepancies were caused by minor constituents that block the body from fully utilizing nutrients. Such antinutritional factors are found in many foods. They include water-soluble pentosans, enzyme inhibitors, alkyl-resorcinols, tannins, acid-detergent fiber, pectins, and protein-polysaccharide complexes. All of these have been found in small amounts in triticale, but at levels much lower than in rye.

The variable results have few or no implications for humans eating triticale because cooking probably removes and certainly reduces the antinutritional factors. Although definitive tests have not been carried out, there are no known ingredients in the grain that differ from those in wheat or rye. Thus, triticale can be used to produce foods similar to those normally made of either wheat or rye.

MILLING PERFORMANCE

Just as bread wheats vary in their genetic potential for quality, varying quality characteristics are found in different triticales. The earliest cultivars had poor milling performance, but improvement of grain plumpness has resulted in many triticales with flour-milling properties similar to those of bread wheats.

Compared with the varieties first released in the 1960s, today's grains are smooth, round, and plump. They pack well and fill space

[8] Khan and Eggum, 1979.

with few voids. This is obvious from the change in "test weight," the weight of a standard volume of seed. The early varieties had test weights of about 60 kg per hectoliter. Today's varieties have test weights up to 78 kg per hectoliter—approaching those of wheat (see figure 3.2).[9]

In general, when triticale is grown on fertile sites and under unstressed conditions, researchers no longer consider shriveled seed to be a concern. However, when it is grown on marginal sites, the seeds are sometimes somewhat shriveled. Thus, at Ciudad Obregón (unstressed growing conditions) one variety may produce seed with a test weight of 78, but the same line at Toluca (stressful conditions) may produce seed with a test weight of only 65. Soon, however, even this is likely to improve. Zebra and Rhino, two CIMMYT lines with stable test weight (that is, whose grains remain plump under both good and bad conditions) are becoming available.

In the past, triticales produced a lower flour yield than bread wheat: their extraction rates were only 50–65 percent, compared with 66–72 percent for bread wheat. This was mainly because of the shriveled grains. Today the situation is quite different: many current triticales have extraction rates of more than 70 percent in laboratory mills.[10] Flour yields of even 73 percent, fully comparable with those of wheat, are found in some advanced lines.

Triticale can be milled either alone or as a mixture with soft bread wheat. In Brazil, triticale is sold as "wheat" and blended with wheat before milling.

FOOD PRODUCTS

For baked products that require doughs or batters with low protein, low water absorption, and minimal resistance to extension, triticale can be fully substituted for wheat flour without modifying the baking methods. Thus, it is highly suited for products in which soft wheat is used. These include cookies, cakes, biscuits, waffles, pancakes, noodles, and flour tortillas.

Unleavened Bread

Unleavened products that have been produced with triticale include the following:

- Chapatis. In tests, a number of triticale lines were as good as or

[9] In British units, the early triticales had test weights of about 50 lb per bushel. Today's varieties have test weights of about 58 and sometimes more than 60. The value for standard wheat is 60 lb per bushel.

[10] Amaya and Skovmand, 1985.

better than the wheat check for making chapatis, a staple flat bread of South Asia.

- Tortillas. Tortillas made from plump triticale kernels taste like those made from wheat. In CIMMYT tests, a number of triticale lines were as good as or better than the wheat check in tortilla-making quality. The triticale tortillas were flavorful, but those made from 100 percent unbleached flour were gray-brown in color. Villagers in Michoacan, Mexico, use triticale daily and report that triticale dough is easier to flatten than wheat dough, making the preparation of tortillas easier. Also, they say, the tortillas hold together better.
- *Concha*. This sweet, whole grain bread, made with molasses, is popular in Mexico. Triticale has been used to make it without any problem.
- *Enjera*. Ethiopians (notably those living outside their native land) have found that triticale flour can be substituted for at least 50 percent of other traditional flours such as teff and buckwheat, used in making the national food, *enjera*. This traditional flat "pancake" can also be made from equal parts of triticale and teff.

Leavened Bread

Flour produced from triticale varieties having breadmaking properties produces rich, brown, satisfactory loaves that look like whole-wheat bread and taste, as their ancestry might suggest, like a combination of rye and wheat bread.

Breads rise because of the presence of special proteins (especially glutens) that trap and hold the bubbles of gas released by the leavening agent. Triticale proteins represent a mixture of the types found in rye and in bread wheat. This is unexpected because many of today's triticales (that is, hexaploids) are made from durum wheats and lack the D-genome chromosomes that are responsible for the breadmaking quality in bread wheats (see chapter 5). Nonetheless, baking trials show that the gluten content is satisfactory and that the dough rises well, at least in some triticale lines. The resulting loaves are of normal size and porosity and have a good flavor.

If the best breadmaking varieties are used, triticale flour by itself can yield good raised breads. Baking tests on advanced triticale lines with plump grains (test weight up to 74 kg per hectoliter) have produced loaves with a volume similar to the loaf volume of the wheat control.[11] However, the absorption, fermentation, and mixing procedures had to be slightly modified from those used with wheat flour. Lowered fermentation temperatures and slightly increased yeast concentrations

[11] Skovmand et al., 1984.

(to compensate for the cooler conditions) were used. With these modifications, and with the progress made by breeders toward plumper grains, there are now many triticale lines that produce excellent loaf volumes, even when 100 percent triticale flour is used to make sandwich bread (see figure 6.2).[12]

By using normal baking methods and run-of-the-mill triticale varieties, many leavened breads can also be made from a 30:70 mixture of triticale and bread wheat with the results equaling those obtained with pure bread wheat.[13] However, with "bread quality" triticale varieties, mixtures of up to 75 percent triticale flour can give products essentially indistinguishable from those made from pure bread-wheat flour.[14] Such blends can be used in industrial bakeries with high-speed mixing equipment. However, as noted in chapter 4, even the best triticales cannot now be used in the pure form in high-speed mixing equipment because of the "sticky dough" problem.

Triticale can also be mixed with non-wheat flours. It combines well with quality-protein maize (QPM), for instance.[15] Both grains contribute lysine to the diet. Breads and muffins made with a blend of QPM and triticale have a nutty flavor and a chewy texture that make their white-flour counterparts seem hopelessly bland by comparison.

Other Foods

Triticale has the potential for use in cereal foods that are not baked—noodles, breakfast cereals, and porridges, for instance. In Kenya, it is already more desirable than wheat for making the traditional staple food, *ugali*, a stiff porridge based on maize meal.

Triticale grain can also be used in the brewing and distilling industries. Based on taste-panel results, it has performed as well as maize and rice, both of which are extensively used by the brewing industry as carbohydrate sources. One large Mexican brewery is growing some 2,000 hectares of the crop near Ciudad Obregón in the state of Sonora to test triticale as a source of malt. Reportedly, triticale's cell-wall polysaccharides (derived from the rye parent) give stability to the foam on the beer.

FEED AND FORAGE

Triticale grain shows considerable potential as livestock feed. Indeed, most of today's yield is used as a feed grain. It has the advantage over

[12] Skovmand et al., 1984.
[13] Unrau and Jenkins, 1964; Sekhon et al., 1980.
[14] R.J. Peña and A. Amaya, CIMMYT, unpublished.
[15] For information on this highly nutritious form of maize, see companion report *Quality-Protein Maize*, National Research Council, 1988.

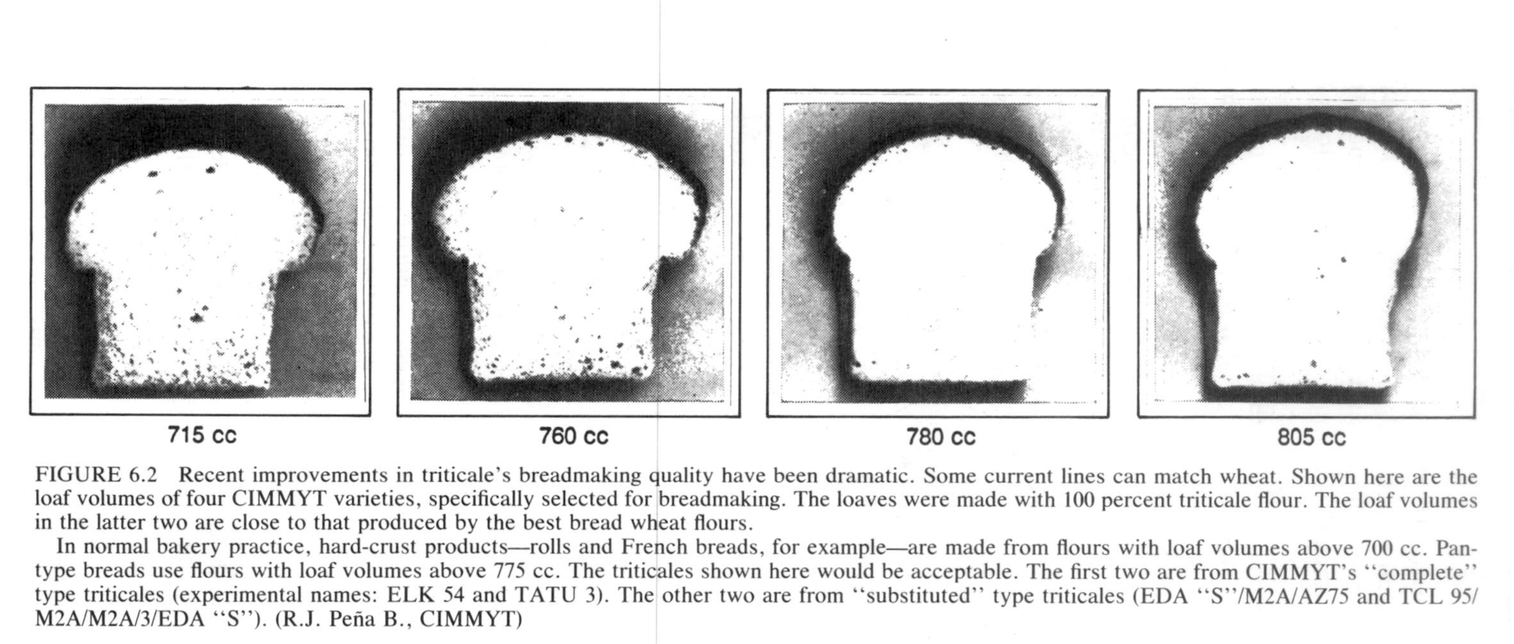

FIGURE 6.2 Recent improvements in triticale's breadmaking quality have been dramatic. Some current lines can match wheat. Shown here are the loaf volumes of four CIMMYT varieties, specifically selected for breadmaking. The loaves were made with 100 percent triticale flour. The loaf volumes in the latter two are close to that produced by the best bread wheat flours.

In normal bakery practice, hard-crust products—rolls and French breads, for example—are made from flours with loaf volumes above 700 cc. Pan-type breads use flours with loaf volumes above 775 cc. The triticales shown here would be acceptable. The first two are from CIMMYT's "complete" type triticales (experimental names: ELK 54 and TATU 3). The other two are from "substituted" type triticales (EDA "S"/M2A/AZ75 and TCL 95/M2A/M2A/3/EDA "S"). (R.J. Peña B., CIMMYT)

rye in that it can be fed directly to animals without prior processing.[16] For pigs, triticale is considered a potentially valuable source of energy and amino acids and is of great potential value where maize and soybeans cannot be grown (as in Poland), or can substitute for rye—which is unsatisfactory for pig or chicken feeds. Several experiments have shown that, whereas rye grain can be fed only at low levels, triticale can be included in rations at up to 50 percent.[17]

In addition to being a feed grain, triticale is particularly promising as an early crop for grazing or making hay. Its forage and silage yields, at least in some situations, can be significantly greater than those of wheat, rye, oats, or barley.[18] It has done well in areas where oats fared poorly, notably where oats proved susceptible to rust. And it persists longer than rye in mixtures with rye grass and clover.[19] Moreover, the protein content of triticale forage ranges between 22 and 24 percent (dry-weight basis), which is higher than that of all other forage grasses except oats.

In one comparison with other small-grain forages, triticale was reported to have the highest forage yield over two years.[20] Grazing trials with yearling steers have shown average daily weight gains of 0.72 kg for triticale, 0.69 kg for wheat, and 0.59 kg for rye.[21]

Winter triticales are particularly promising as forages. Argentina, one of the world's largest producers of triticale for forage, has several (so far unnamed) forage lines that are used by farmers. They have been selected under heavy grazing by sheep and are derived from crosses of spring and winter triticales.

Improved forage varieties can be expected in the future. There is much potential for selecting for higher protein and better grain. There is also a possibility of combining forage production with grain production. In the Andalusian region of Spain in 1982—the driest year in the recorded history of this region—the wheat crop was so stricken it had to be abandoned. Animals were turned onto triticale instead, and allowed to graze it down twice. Then came late winter rains, and the farmers allowed the triticale to produce seed. At the end of the season, they still harvested 2.5 tons of grain per hectare.[22]

[16] Rye grain must be soaked in hot water to destroy antinutritional factors in the seed coat before it is fed to livestock.
[17] Batterham, 1966.
[18] Bishnoi et al., 1978.
[19] Bertrand and Dunavin, 1974.
[20] Bishnoi and Patel, 1979. The variety used was AM2855.
[21] Rossi, 1979.
[22] Information from G. Varughese.

Because triticale is similar to other feed grains, price and yield will often be the factors to determine its utilization in animal feeds. In this respect, triticale often has a competitive advantage, especially where growing conditions are marginal for the conventional feed grains (see figure 7.1).

7
Experiences Around the World

. . . [T]here are some 230 million rural households in Africa, Asia, and Latin America that have been bypassed by the green revolution—men and women living on marginal land not appropriate for growing wheat or rice and without access to money for the special inputs necessary for green-revolution farming. This group of nearly 1.4 billion people in the Third World holds the key to future increases in world food production.

EDWARD C. WOLF
Beyond the Green Revolution

Earlier chapters have briefly noted some examples of triticale cultivation. These and other experiences around the world are presented here in more detail. This sampling contains only some of the important cases known to the writers when this report was prepared and is not meant to be encyclopedic or definitive.

NORTH AMERICA[1]

Canada

As previously stated, Canadian scientists were the first to convert what was largely a biological oddity into a practical crop. In 1954, at the University of Manitoba, plant breeders L.H. Shebeski and B.C. Jenkins began selecting hexaploid triticales that were light-insensitive, early maturing, and resistant to diseases (particularly stem rust). Dwarf and semi-dwarf wheat lines were used as a source of stronger straw. This brought marked agronomic improvements to the crop.

At the same time, feed-quality evaluations proved that triticale grain was suitable for use in cattle, sheep, and poultry rations, and it was this combination of plant breeding and grain-quality evaluation that established, once and for all, that triticale could be a commercial reality, not just a genetic aberration of purely academic interest.

In 1969, the Manitoba researchers released Rosner, the cultivar that established triticale as a farm crop in Canada. Results from feeding trials, distilling and brewing tests, and experimental manufacture of breakfast cereals indicated that it had considerable potential. Rosner

[1] Information on triticale in the United States is given in Appendix A.

and another variety called "Welsh" came to be grown on up to 10,000 hectares annually.[2] Both, however, suffered from shriveled seed, premature sprouting, and erratic yields.

In subsequent years, sizable triticale breeding programs were continued in Manitoba as well as in Saskatchewan and Quebec. Smaller ones were maintained in Alberta, Ontario, and Prince Edward Island. Yields were raised dramatically; however, all the varieties produced had problems as grain crops, including low fertility and ergot infection.

As a result, many people concluded that triticale was an impossible dream. Therefore, interest in the crop as a cereal grain for Canada declined. Only minor production now exists. In 1986, for instance, insufficient triticale grain was available for milling. Sad to say, the University of Manitoba program that initiated almost all of today's worldwide triticale developments was discontinued in 1985 when its funds were cut off. Currently, Canada's biggest triticale research program is at Lacombe, Alberta; a small program also continues at the University of Guelph in Ontario.

Despite the drop in official interest, Canadian farmers still grow triticale for silage because it can be harvested before or after other crops, thereby allowing the farmers to use their time and machinery more efficiently. The variety called "Carman" now occupies 95 percent of the triticale fields in Western Canada.

EUROPE

Triticale development programs are proceeding in many European countries, including Bulgaria, Czechoslovakia, East Germany, France, Greece, Hungary, Italy, the Netherlands, Poland, Portugal, Romania, the Soviet Union, Spain, Sweden, the United Kingdom, and Yugoslavia. Only a few countries, however, have made substantial commitments to the crop so far. Among these are the following.

France

Since 1958, France has had several triticale research programs. Breeding work at Clermont Ferrand (initiated in the 1960s) culminated in the release of the variety Clercal in 1980. As a result of its success, many research centers and private companies are now involved in producing and promoting triticale (see Appendix C). The variety Lasko, introduced from Poland in the 1970s, is also grown on considerable commercial hectarage.

---

[2] Welsh resulted from several generations of reselection of a CIMMYT F_2 line that reached Canada via California.

FIGURE 7.1 Triticale in Poland. Poland's embrace of triticale as a way to upgrade the productivity of marginal areas seems a likely forerunner of future experiences throughout the world. Triticale is becoming an excellent rye replacement. It both yields well and finds a ready market. The photograph shows a field of triticale (cultivar Grado) at the Zaborówek state farm near Warsaw. (W. W. Wozniak)

Poland[3]

With five million hectares of "problem" soils, Poland devotes to rye a higher proportion of its cereal production than any other country in the world. (In 1985, 3,083,000 hectares were under rye; only 1,855,000 were under wheat.) This is because rye thrives where soils are too acid, too sandy, or too low in phosphorus for wheat and barley to grow well. The problem, however, is that although Poland can grow rye well, it can neither absorb nor export as much as it can produce. Thus, most of the production goes for animal feed, chiefly pig feed, despite the low feeding value caused by low protein content and growth-inhibiting factors.

Because triticale offered a more acceptable grain than rye, intensive breeding started in Poland in 1968. It was oriented chiefly towards finding types that would grow on sandy soils of medium fertility. It produced three cultivars: Lasko, Grado, and Dagro, all registered between 1982 and 1985. These are now widely grown not only in Poland, but in several Western European countries and New Zealand. Lasko, in particular, has proved highly adaptable and is currently the most widely grown triticale in the world.

Polish researchers have concentrated on producing winter triticales. This is because the frequent occurrence of dry summers and delayed

[3] This section is based largely on information from T. Wolski.

springs in Poland means that winter cereals are more reliable than spring ones.

In general, Polish triticales have a good tolerance to acid soils and soluble aluminum, and show good resistance to mildew and rusts. Their nutritional value is equal to that of wheat for feeding poultry, and it is higher than that of barley for feeding pigs. They have broad adaptation because they were selected in an environment where climate varies greatly between years as well as between regions.

Because of its promising features, triticale has captured enormous farmer interest in Poland. The 1986 fall plantings covered an amazing 309,000 hectares, but the 1987 plantings were almost twice that (600,000 hectares). According to official plans, by 1990 the plantings should reach 1 million hectares.

Triticale is a good substitute for rye on richer and medium-fertile soils. In addition, in some areas (especially those with acid soils and where mildew and rust infection can be heavy and the possibility of chemical control is limited) it is competitive with wheat. Yields have proved superior to the most widely grown rye and wheat cultivars in state trials. Triticale costs more to produce than rye, owing to the indispensable need for herbicides. It costs less than wheat, however, as it needs less fertilizer and fungicide. Winter triticales give similar yields to wheat on a lower level of nitrogen fertilization (a normal saving is 20–30 kg per hectare).

In the near future, the large-scale baking of triticale bread is foreseen. To reduce purchases abroad, Polish law requires that imported wheat flour be blended with locally grown flours. In the past this meant adding rye, but in the future it will mean adding triticale because it is better for baking bread.

Soviet Union

For some years, the Soviet Union has officially fostered the planting of triticale. The area devoted to the crop expanded from 27,000 hectares in 1977 to about 250,000 hectares today. The plant is now a common sight in the fields of the Ukraine, the Kuban, and Stavropol territories, in the Chuvash and Mari Autonomous Soviet Socialist Republics, and in the Voronezh, Moscow, and Pskov regions.

The Ukrainian Research Institute for the Growth, Breeding, and Genetics of Plants in Kharkov has increased triticale yields some 18–20 percent over that of the most widely used Soviet variety of soft winter wheat (Mironovskaya–808). At the same time, the triticale has 1.5–2 percent more protein than ordinary wheat, and 3–4 percent more than rye. With resistance to drought and to winter frosts, the Kharkov triticales reportedly suit the climatic conditions of the Ukraine, the

Russian Midlands, and the south of Russia. Most or all of these are winter triticales.

For use in more arid areas, the Institute of Physiology and Biophysics of the Academy of Sciences of the Tajik SSR has produced a different set of triticales. These are mainly spring triticales, and they are said to tolerate increased concentrations of salt in the soil—a particularly important feature in irrigated farm fields in Soviet Central Asia, where high evaporation rates tend to induce salination. They are also said to yield two to three times as much fodder as wheat under those conditions.

Hungary

Hungary played a distinguished part in triticale's development. In 1954, Arpad Kiss opened the way to secondary triticales by crossing octoploids with hexaploids.[4] Kiss noted that his products had several superior properties, and by 1968 he had varieties suitable for release to farmers. These were among the first triticale varieties to be grown commercially anywhere in the world. As early as 1969, about 40,000 hectares were under cultivation. When conditions were favorable, they yielded up to 7 tons of grain per hectare, and this outstanding performance is credited with stimulating triticale cultivation throughout Europe.

Spain

Spain was also one of the first countries to release triticale for cultivation. The Cachirulo variety came out in 1968. However, because of difficulties with threshing and lack of markets, little production occurred. In 1979, a variety that was easier to thresh and that yielded better was released under the name "Manigero." Since then, Spain has approved several improved varieties for cultivation, many of them based on CIMMYT germplasm. Today, it annually grows more than 30,000 hectares of fall-sown, spring-habit triticale, and the area is expanding.

Portugal

Portugal is overly dependent on cereal imports. In the last few years it has produced only 25 percent of the grains required to feed its people and livestock. Unfortunately, most Portuguese soils are poor, with low levels of organic matter and phosphorus. As much as 80 percent of the soils are acidic (pH below 5.5). Moreover, lacking water resources for irrigation, almost all crops must be rainfed, and the amount and

[4] The initial hybrids were heptaploids from which the D-genome chromosomes from the bread-wheat parent were eliminated after a few generations to leave the secondary hexaploids.

distribution of rainfall are highly erratic. For this reason, rye has always been important to Portugal, and triticale, therefore, would appear to have much to offer as an upgrade crop.

Since 1969, the National Plant Breeding Station of Elvas (ENMP) has conducted a triticale breeding program. More recently, a second program has been established at the University of Trás-os-Môntes e Alto Douro. In both cases, germplasm from CIMMYT has shown excellent potential. Five CIMMYT varieties—Armadillo, Arabian, Bacum, Beagle, and Mapache—are now in cultivation.

The results have been so outstanding that the area under triticale is constantly increasing. The current estimate is 80,000 hectares nationwide. In the province of Trás-os-Môntes e Alto Douro, traditional rye country, the first triticale variety was approved in 1987; it, too, is expected to increase dramatically.

So far, the best productivity has been obtained with substitution-type triticales. However, because complete types are more stable and better adapted to poor soils and difficult environments, they are expected to be increasingly used in the future. A major problem has been lodging, which occurs under good productivity conditions. Efforts are being made to rectify this.

So far, triticale has resisted various diseases and pests much better than wheat. However, as a precaution against possible future outbreaks, the breeders each year inoculate the triticales in their nurseries with rusts and blotches (*Septoria* spp.), using inoculum collected from triticale. Breadmaking quality of all the advanced lines are systematically analyzed every year in collaboration with the laboratory of the Cereal Board of Portugal.

Triticale seems to have an assured place in Portuguese agriculture. The area devoted to it is likely to continue increasing because the support price is similar to that of grade-II wheat, yet its productivity is better under poor soils and low rainfall, and it is more reliable in bad years.

AFRICA

Only one African country, South Africa, reports having a full triticale program. Others, such as Algeria, Egypt, Kenya, Tanzania, and Zambia, have undertaken agronomic research and food-technology testing. Some others are evaluating new germplasm in an exploratory manner.

ASIA

China, Indonesia, and South Korea have also undertaken considerable triticale development, while India, Iran, Pakistan, and Syria maintain breeding, testing, cereal technology, and other triticale investigations. The most interesting developments to date have been in China.

China

In southwestern China, on the highlands of the Yunnan-Sichuan plateau, successful cultivation and utilization of octoploid triticale is under way. There, just north of Burma, triticale has opened up a new possibility for increased cereal production in mountain areas at between 1,800 and 2,600 m above sea level.

The region has a cold climate, a short frost-free period, and dry, alkaline soil. Traditionally, buckwheat and oats were grown, but these yield poorly and are replaced wherever possible. In 1970, a strain of rye with good yield and cold resistance was introduced; however, its flour-milling quality was poor. The Chinese Academy of Agriculture and Forestry then offered the local peasants 10 selected triticale lines. Despite a severe drought during the 1973 growing season, 8 of the 10 triticales gave better harvests than the local rye and wheat. One yielded 20 percent more than rye and 61 percent more than two local wheat strains.

Subsequently, 42 production teams conducted experiments with triticale on this mountainous land, on both poor and fertile soils. Yields averaged 2.13 tons per hectare, considerably more than either buckwheat or ryes. These octoploid triticales were also more winter hardy, more adaptable to poor soils, and more resistant to drought and lodging.

SOUTH AMERICA

Reports from Brazil show many activities in triticale. Argentina also has a full program, and Colombia and Ecuador have small programs.

Brazil[5]

Triticale has been under observation in Brazil since 1969; lines with acceptable grain were first obtained in 1976. Since then, yield potentials have been assessed through the Brazilian Triticale Yield Nursery, a series of comparisons carried out at as many as 27 locations. All Brazilian triticales are derived from CIMMYT germplasm.

Most trials in the states of Paraná and Rio Grande do Sul have shown high yields with acceptable test weights. As a result, five

[5] This section based on a paper by A.C. Baier and J.L. Nedel (see Research Contacts).

varieties were released for commercial use during 1985.[6] Irrigated trials in the central Brazilian savannas (*Cerrados*) have given the highest yields and test weights.

The cultivated triticale area was 1,500 hectares in 1984, 4,500 in 1985, 20,000 in 1986, and about 30,000 in 1987. Triticale has shown good adaptation to Brazil's acid soils and has demonstrated high resistance to mildew, leaf blotch (*Septoria*), stem rust, and leaf rust. The main disease problems have been head diseases (*Septoria*, *Helminthosporium*, and scab), premature sprouting, and low test weight. Farmers have obtained good responses to nitrogen top-dressing during tillering and to systemic fungicides at flowering.

Grain quality has been investigated in both laboratories and commercial facilities. Milling quality has proved similar to that of wheat. Good crackers, cookies, and pastas are being produced using 100 percent triticale flour. In commerce, triticale flour is already being substituted for wheat flour (from 10 to 35 percent) in the manufacture of several types of bread.

Since 1986, the official triticale price has been set at the same price as wheat. Also, the same standards are used for both crops.

PACIFIC

In the South Pacific region, Australia has four major triticale breeding programs and New Zealand has one.

Australia

Since 1979, Australia has released 15 triticale varieties for farmers. The crop has been rapidly adopted. In 1979, the area planted stood at about 22,000 hectares; in 1985–86 approximately 160,000 hectares of triticale were cultivated.[7] In fact, since 1983, the Australian triticale crop has been larger than the Australian cotton or rice crops.

The rapid adoption of the crop was because of high yield in some areas, notably those with acid soils, the existence of a ready market for stockfeed grain, and the fact that direct farmer-to-manufacturer sales were possible.[8]

---

[6] The five were BR 1 (PFT 766), CEP 15-Batovi (TCEP 77138), IAPAR 13-Araucaria (TPOLO 8432), OCEPAR 1 (TOC 807), and OCEPAR 2 (ITOC 841).

[7] Australian Institute of Agricultural Science, 1986. *Proceedings of the International Triticale Symposium*, Sydney. p. 150.

[8] Australian farmers are, in general, required to sell their wheat and barley through statutory marketing authorities, and normally are not fully paid for their crop until some time after harvest. Because triticale is not subject to such controls, Australian growers can negotiate their own direct sales and receive payment on delivery.

On good soils in the eastern wheat belt, triticale has fallen short of the best wheat yields by 5–15 percent in more than 16 trials since 1978.[9] On poor, light land, however, triticale has substantially outyielded wheat. For instance, in the Merredin area of Western Australia, on five sites chosen for their acid soils, triticales yielded 50 percent more than wheats. In the Pilliga-scrub region of northern New South Wales, trial plantings of wheat failed to produce grain because of soil acidity, but the neighboring triticale plantings yielded 2.5 tons of grain per hectare.

There are currently triticale breeding programs in New South Wales, Victoria, South Australia, and Western Australia. Those in Victoria, New South Wales, and Western Australia use mainly CIMMYT-derived materials. South Australia, on the other hand, is making its own triticales, concentrating on a range of durum wheats and cereal ryes including South Australia rye, which has long been used to stabilize sand dunes in the state. South Australia's goal is to create triticales with adaptation to marginal conditions. More than 400 different primary triticales were created this way.[10]

Since the occurrence in 1982 and 1984 of new stem-rust strains that proved virulent on all but one of the current cultivars, selection for resistance to stem rust has become a major priority in Australian breeding and selection programs.

Two forage cultivars—one purely for grazing, and one dual purpose (grazing and grain)—have recently been released by the University of New England, Armidale, New South Wales.

An Interstate Triticale Yield Trial, with trial sites in every Australian state, is currently in its eighth year. Triticale is showing excellent adaptation to wheat soils that are becoming acidified because of the long and continuous use of subterranean clover and phosphate fertilizer.

Most Australian triticale is used locally to feed poultry, pigs, cattle, and sheep, although some of it is exported to Southeast Asia. However, its use in human food has begun, and a triticale cookbook containing more than 100 recipes has been published.[11]

[9] Skovmand et al., 1984.
[10] Information from K.V. Cooper.
[11] Cooper, 1985.

8
Research Needs

In the last five decades, and mostly in the last two, research has transformed triticale from a taxonomic anomaly into a commercial crop. In a historical sense, the progress has been phenomenal: triticale can, under certain circumstances, match the performance of wheat, which has been under development for at least 10,000 years. Despite this progress, however, triticale is no miracle. Uncertainties and problems persist and, to varying degrees, need to be illuminated and overcome by research. Some of these are highlighted in this chapter.

FIELD TRIALS

Triticale is so new that in many of the environments where it is most promising, it is little known. A range of different cultivars needs to be tested and the most appropriate ones selected for local adaptation. These environments include the grain-growing areas with acid and alkaline soils, recurrent droughts, changeable weather, and high disease pressures.

Specific Third World regions where triticale trials should be conducted include:

- The highlands of eastern Africa;
- Much of North Africa (Algeria, Morocco, and Libya, for example);
- The Himalayan zone (particularly in the northern rim of Pakistan and India), Cambodia, and Thailand, where soils are acid;
- Tibet, other inland areas of China, and Sumatra (particularly sites where there are both acid soils and extended dry seasons);
- The *Cerrados* (acid soil) region of Brazil;
- The highlands of Central and South America; and
- Droughty zones in the Middle East (such as Syria).

GENETICS AND BREEDING

Broadening the Gene Pool

For practical reasons, CIMMYT's triticale breeders had to rely entirely on the genetic endowment of Armadillo. It was this variety that produced the fertile lines with plump seeds (see chapter 2). However, this huge benefit also had a drawback—it was a genetic bottleneck that left CIMMYT triticales with a narrow gene base.

Now is the time to broaden the base of the CIMMYT triticale germplasm. A huge potential exists for this: some 200,000 wheats exist in the world's collections; fewer than 1 percent have ever been used in making primary triticales. (Indeed, all of today's advanced triticales come from only a handful of wheats.) There is also a massive gene pool on the *rye* side. It is particularly vital to explore this because rye is the parent that endows triticale with the resilience and adaptation to difficult environmental conditions.

Disease Resistance

Although diseases have not been devastating as yet, it is reasonable to expect that they will increase in severity. Good opportunities exist to counter this. On the one hand, triticale benefits indirectly from the ongoing production of disease-resistant wheats. This is because most triticale diseases also occur in wheat, and resistance located in wheat can usually be transferred (leaf-rust resistance is a good example). On the other hand, triticale can also benefit from its rye parent. Resistance to many diseases is inherent in the rye plant and can be transferred to triticale. However, this usually takes considerable effort.[1]

Triticale's resistance to bunts and smuts provides an advantage for the crop, but at higher elevations the possibility of ergot problems introduces a new uncertainty that will have to be evaluated on a case-by-case basis.

A particular immediate need is to select triticales with solid stems. These would confer resistance to sawfly and stem borer. A good start has already been made, and both CIMMYT and Bulgarian researchers have developed experimental solid-stem triticale lines.

Agronomic Improvements

Perhaps the most important agronomic requirement is to select for early maturity. This trait helps the crop escape end-of-season diseases

[1] The situation is actually more complex than is implied here. Most triticale characters, some disease resistance included, are not directly inherited from wheat and rye, but depend on interactions. Information from T. Wolski.

and climatic stresses. Currently, the long period between flowering and seed maturity is hindering triticale's acceptance. However, early types are becoming available (see figure 3.4).

The crop's yields could rise dramatically if it were repartitioned to emphasize grain over foliage. Because the plant produces more total dry matter than wheat, it would seem, theoretically, to have a higher yield potential. Repartitioning to emphasize grain over leaves and stems may push its yields well above those that are achievable today.

Although triticale lines with relatively high test weights exist, these tend to be among the lowest yielding. More development is needed to ensure that the types with the most desirable grain structure are also the highest producing.

To eliminate the lodging problem completely, there is a need to improve straw strength and to overcome crown weakness.

Sprouting

Preharvest sprouting is a limitation still to be solved if CIMMYT triticales are to be grown successfully in humid or rainy sites. Where conditions are dry at harvest time, few of these lines ever sprout, but where conditions at harvest are damp, many sprout unacceptably.

Australian farmers have found that where rains occur late in the growing season, the seeds absorb water. Even brief showers can lead to soft grains and shriveling. Research has shown that the feed value is unaffected, but the wrinkled and bleached appearance and loose seed coat destroy the grain's market acceptability.

This bleaching has also been noted in Canada, western Oregon, North Dakota, and elsewhere where brief rains occur after the grain has ripened. The problem is being slowly overcome as hard-seeded types become available, but more concentrated research is needed to eliminate it entirely.

Octoploid Triticales

Octoploids deserve more attention, particularly because their bread wheat parent is likely to lead to new triticales with excellent baking qualities.

Hybrid Triticales

A development that may project triticale to the forefront of cereals is the possibility of intraspecific hybrids.[2] Many first-generation (F_1) crosses between two different triticale lines produce plump seeds;

[2] This section is based on information from R. Metzger.

given intense study, it should be possible to produce them for commercial use.[3] Creating such intraspecific hybrids involves the same problems as making hybrid wheat (something long sought, so far without commercial success), but triticale produces pollen prolifically, and might be more successful.

This is a long shot, but research to explore the mechanisms of producing hybrids is warranted. Among the relatives of wheat are several in whose cytoplasms wheat becomes male sterile, and it would not be surprising if one or more of these would sterilize triticale as well. Then it would only be necessary to find fertility-restoring genes, perhaps transferred from the contributor of the cytoplasm, that override the effect of the alien cytoplasm on fertility.

NUTRITION AND FOOD USES

The plant's wide genetic variability offers many opportunities for improving the grain's nutritional qualities. Chemical and nutritional screening techniques should be developed that can easily identify nutritionally superior types at early stages of selection, and on a mass-screening basis. The techniques should be sensitive enough that individual seeds can be sampled without being destroyed. The desirable ones can then be planted.

Antinutritional Factors

Although chemical and biological data are still incomplete, and in fact are sometimes conflicting, it appears that the most recent triticale varieties can form up to at least 50 percent of the cereal base in the diets of pigs and poultry without causing nutritional problems (see chapter 6).

Nonetheless, research is needed to identify and establish the substances responsible for the conflicting biological performance in animal-feeding trials. This knowledge may allow researchers to select lines that are low in antinutritional factors. Also, it will allow researchers to study the fate of antinutritional factors in various processing methods.

Feeding Trials

Controlled animal studies are needed using well-characterized triticales to quantify protein digestibility, absorption, and other practical

[3] Triticale itself is a hybrid, but it is a stable one created by lengthy selection, so that it breeds true generation after generation. What is being suggested here is a hybrid of the type analogous to corn hybrids. In this case, two diverse lines are crossed, and the seed is marketed directly for one-season use.

nutritional details on varieties that are being released for production. Further, there is a need to check to ensure that normal processing procedures do not overly damage the nutritional quality.

End-Use Research

Insufficient attention has been paid to end uses. At this time, triticale can act as a substitute for wheat, but no unique market has yet been developed. As a result, most triticale now sells in the least profitable grain markets—animal feed, for example.

Research funds should be spent on improving triticale's quality for leavened bread and other premium uses. The goal should be to keep all the genes for hardiness, disease resistance, and tolerance to adverse soils while upgrading the grain's performance, especially in raised breads in large-scale bakeries.

One basic limitation, as previously noted, is the "sticky dough" problem. Among the gliadin proteins, which cause bread to rise, is one whose production is controlled by a gene on chromosome 1R. This particular gliadin is believed to cause the dough to stick to the high-speed mixing equipment used in industrial bakeries. If the 1R gene is really at fault, its modification or even its elimination (perhaps by genetic engineering) could solve the problem.

It seems likely that chromosomal constitutions may be found that could enhance the breadmaking characteristics of hexaploid triticales even more. For example, it might be possible to select ones with the AADDRR or BBDDRR constitutions or various combinations of A and B chromosomes with DDRR.[4]

Actually, it should only be necessary to introduce chromosome 1D to improve breadmaking quality. Substituting 1D for 1R may not be desirable, however, because of 1R's possible favorable effect on yield as well as disease resistance, but substituting 1D for 1B or 1A might be successful.[5] Of course, chromosome insertion is no guarantee of success; gene expression after insertion is the ultimate test.

TRITICALE AS A GENETIC BRIDGE

As noted previously, triticale can be used to improve both wheat and rye because it can be backcrossed to either of its parental species. In this regard, it offers a conduit for gene transfer between the two. In fact, the situation is already getting to the point where wheat and rye are one continuous gene pool.

---

[4] Müntzing, 1979.
[5] Information from E. Sears.

Spontaneous crosses of wheat and rye have occurred many times in the past and some chromosome segments from rye have been naturally translocated to wheat chromosomes. Such wheat/rye translocations are used in wheats throughout the world as well as in the Veery wheats developed by CIMMYT. While it is theoretically possible that nature can introduce wheat chromosome segments into rye, this has not been demonstrated so far. However, by passing through triticale as an intermediary, both processes may be made a routine part of both wheat breeding and rye breeding.

OTHER WIDE CROSSES

Triticale's progress from a curiosity to the threshold of global commercial cultivation encourages the hope that other such "wide crosses" will soon follow. The possibility of blending the genes of disparate genera has, at least in speculation, long appealed to plant scientists as a powerful tool.

The implications of this are far reaching. The development of fertile triticale suggests that the unbreakable laws of nature that keep different genera apart can at least be bent. And through this process breeders might be able to custom-tailor many more cereals to specific human

IMPROVEMENT OF WHEAT

In the past, many wheat breeders have viewed triticale as a competitor and potential usurper. However, triticale is an excellent source of genes for adding to wheat. The two crops share so many genes that in future they may be seen as a single extended gene pool. For wheat breeders triticale could become a helper to be employed when appropriate, not viewed as a rival to be shunned.

For example, rye genes have been transferred from rye to wheat via triticale, thereby producing wheats that grow better in copper-deficient soils.* Also, a "triticale bridge" has been used to transfer disease resistance from rye to wheat. One example is the transference of resistance to cereal cyst nematode (a major problem of wheat growers in Mediterranean climates).**

In future, triticale may provide the solution to the fungal disease called "take-all"—the single worst wheat disease in Australia and several other leading wheat-growing nations. Wheat is highly susceptible to this disease and contains no known sources of resistance. Rye, on the other hand, is highly resistant. Triticale might be the link that allows the genes to be brought into wheat.

* Information from K. Shepherd and R. Graham.
** Information from K. Shepherd and I. Dundas.

needs and to special agricultural niches. Some possibilities within the cereals are briefly mentioned here (see also table 8.1).

Wheat x Wheatgrass

It is known that wheat can be crossed with wheatgrasses (*Agropyron* species). Grains of the resulting hybrid, which has been called "agrotricum," have high lysine contents. A few have been grown as forage crops. They have been widely used by wheat breeders around the world as sources of resistance to diseases and environmental stress.[6] At CIMMYT and in Sweden, these crosses are being used in attempts to improve kernel quality in triticale. Agrotricum strains with high kernel quality have already been obtained, but so far their undesirable properties have kept them from being released to farmers.[7]

In an attempt to create perennial wheat in the 1930s, an agrotricum (called "W–21") was developed by the United States Department of Agriculture. It resulted from crossing bread wheat with tall wheatgrass (*Agropyron elongatum*). The researchers were about three years from releasing the variety for food use when the project was dropped. However, the germplasm was saved, and today this hybrid is grown as a winter cover and food for game birds. The plant should be reinvestigated. It is weakly perennial, surviving 2–3 years where winters are mild. Yields of up to 2,200 kg per hectare have been obtained in plots in Pennsylvania.[8,9] The perennial trait is valuable because the land does not have to be plowed and exposed to potential erosion each year.

Wheat x Self-Fertile Rye

In the 1970s, it was recommended that self-fertile common ryes or wild ryes (*Secale vavilovii* and *S. silvestre*) be tried as parents of triticale.[10] The rationale is that self-sterile ryes are highly heterozygous and commonly carry deleterious genes (in heterozygous condition), some of which become homozygous in triticale and presumably result in reduced vigor and/or fertility. The self-fertile species should have

---

[6] For example, at the University of California, Davis, wheatgrass is being used to bestow increased salt tolerance on wheat.

[7] Transferring their fine kernel quality to triticale would be of immense value. Gustafson, 1974.

[8] Information from Rodale Research Center, R.D. 1, Box 323, Kutztown, Pennsylvania 19530. Seed is available from Kester's Wild Game Food Nursery, P.O. Box V, Omro, Wisconsin 54963, USA.

[9] Similar attempts to develop perennial wheats were made in the USSR, but as yet no perennial cereals are commercially available. Tritsin, 1960.

[10] Qualset et al., 1976; Müntzing, 1979.

TABLE 8.1 Some Promising Cereal Hybrids for the Future.

Common Name	Parents of Hybrid: Maternal	Paternal	Attributes
Tritordeum	*Hordeum chilense*	*Triticum turgidum*	high protein
Tritordeum	*Hordeum chilense*	*Triticum polonicum*	high protein
Tritordeum	*Hordeum californicum*	*Triticum aestivum*	soil acidity tolerance
Tritordeum	*Triticum timopheevi*	*Hordeum bogdanii*	undetermined
Agrotricum	*Triticum turgidum*	*Agropyron distichum*	virus resistance salt tolerance
Agrotricum	*Triticum aestivum*	*Agropyron distichum*	virus resistance salt tolerance leaf-rust resistance stem-rust resistance
Agrotricum	*Triticum aestivum*	*Agropyron elongatum*	salt tolerance protein content large seed early heading enhanced tillering
Agrotricum	*Triticum aestivum*	*Agropyron intermedium*	stem-rust resistance leaf-rust resistance stripe-rust resistance streak-mosaic resistance virus resistance leaf pubescence cold hardiness
Agrotricum	*Triticum turgidum*	*Agropyron elongatum*	
Agrotricum	*Triticum timopheevi*	*Agropyron elongatum*	
Agrotricum	*Triticum turgidum*	*Agropyron intermedium*	
Agrotricum	*Triticum aestivum*	*Agropyron junceum*	salt tolerance
Agrotricum	*Triticum aestivum*	*Agropyron rechingeri*	

SOURCE: G. Fedak (see Research Contacts).

less heterozygosity and consequently should retain fewer of the deleterious recessives. So far, triticales made by crossing wheat and *S. vavilovii* have proven to have very low fertility. When self-fertile selections of common rye have been inbred, with selection for vigor and fertility, and then combined with wheat, the results have been sufficiently encouraging that further work in this direction seems to be justified.[11]

Wheat x *Elymus*

Wheat can also be crossed with grasses of the genus *Elymus*.[12] The resulting plants are especially interesting because they produce excep-

[11] Müntzing, 1979.
[12] Cicin, 1972.

tionally large spikes, containing up to about 200 spikelets. They are also somewhat fertile. Incomplete amphiploids with 42 chromosomes—comprising the wheat genomes A and B and one of the two genomes of *Elymus*—have been found. If the number of seeds set per spike can be raised, this line of research may lead to new, extremely high-yielding grain crops.

Barley x Other Grasses

Many intergeneric hybrids between barley (both cultivated and wild) and other grasses have been made in Australia, Canada, the United States, and elsewhere. These have included crosses between various barleys and wheat, rye, triticale, wheatgrass, ryegrass, and *Psathyrostachys* species.[13] The first barley x wheat cross of consequence was made in Australia, where six of the seven possible wheat/barley addition lines (each with one pair of barley chromosomes added to wheat) were produced.[14] These hybrids are potentially interesting because there are surely characteristics of barley—at least disease resistance—that would be useful if transferred to wheat. They provide a means to transfer barley characteristics to wheat.

Wheat x *Aegilops* Species

Tschermak, the person who named triticale in 1935 (see chapter 2), made hybrids between many different cereals. For instance, he succeeded in producing an amphidiploid between tetraploid wheat and *Aegilops ovata*, which he named *Aegilotricum*.[15] This opened the way for transfer of variability through interspecific hybridization. The possible future importance of this is that numerous *Aegilops* species are crossable with wheat and they have a great variety of characteristics. Many are resistant to all or nearly all the diseases of wheat. Some have the D-genome, from which genes can easily be transferred; others, less closely related to wheat, will require complex but already established cytogenetic methods for transfer of genes to wheat. Alternatively, molecular biological methods, not yet in place for wheat, give promise for transference of some kinds of genes.

---

[13] Information from George Fedak, Research Branch Agriculture Canada, Ottawa, Ontario, Canada K1A 0C6.
[14] Islam and Shepherd, 1980.
[15] Tschermak and Bleier, 1926.

Appendix A

Triticale's Future in the United States

This report highlights triticale's potential for benefiting developing nations. However, wheat is planted on more acres than any other crop in the United States (which produced more than two billion bushels in 1986). Despite the major domestic and foreign markets for U.S. wheat, the nation has the capacity to vastly increase production by bringing back into cultivation some 30–50 million acres set aside under government programs, many of which could produce small grains, including triticale. Accordingly, this brief section outlines the crop's domestic promise.[1]

Triticale has had a checkered history in the United States. Initially, it was described by overenthusiastic, perhaps unscrupulous, entrepreneurs as a high-yielding, high-protein crop with huge potential markets. In the 1960s, farmers eagerly tried it. At one point there were almost 250,000 acres growing in states from New York to California.

This, in turn, stimulated many experiment stations to evaluate triticale, but their research lagged far behind the crop's momentum. That was unfortunate because the varieties being released to farmers had serious deficiencies. With few exceptions, they fell short of the yields and grain quality of the best-adapted wheat varieties. This was not unexpected, since little effort had been devoted to adapting various triticales to America's different climatic regions. Nonetheless, the effects were devastating; interest in the crop promptly collapsed.

However, despite the lack of commercial interest, a few breeders continued developing new experimental lines. They focused on kernel conformation, floret fertility, tillering ability, standability, winter hardiness, disease resistance, and fertilizer response. Most used lines developed at the Centro Internacional de Mejoramiento de Maíz y Trigo (CIMMYT) or at the Jenkins Foundation for Research of Salinas, California. A few used lines from Poland or Canada.

As a result of several decades of research and testing by this small group of diehards, slow but steady advances have been made. Today's

[1] Whereas the rest of the report uses metric units, here we use the units most meaningful to American readers involved in farming and agribusiness.

Harvesting the 1988 triticale crop, The Dalles, Oregon. On the alkaline soils of the Pacific northwest, triticale is establishing itself as a part of the agricultural scene. (T. Jewett, *The Oregonian*)

triticale varieties are far better than those of a decade ago. They are very tolerant of smuts. Their kernels are much more dense, although test weights are still sometimes a little low (55 lb per bushel). Also, they have much higher fertility, although sometimes sterility is still a problem.

These advances have gone largely unreported, but lines that are superior to wheat in one or more agronomic characters are already available. For instance, experimental lines selected for adaptation to northern California have produced 27 percent more grain than the highest yielding wheat check. Other lines, selected for adaptation to northern Texas and to the southeastern states, have produced 11 percent more grain than the wheat check. And in the northwest, types that outyield wheat on highly alkaline soils are available.

Such advances have so far failed to raise national enthusiasm for triticale as a food crop because throughout the 1980s the United States has been drowning in a surplus of wheat and has been struggling to suppress grain production. However, following the drought of 1988, that attitude appears likely to change. In the 1990s, triticale could once again attract widespread interest because it is a resilient crop, useful in harsh and changeable conditions.

As such, triticale is one of the most promising alternative crops for the nation. It does well in stressful environments that keep wheat from reaching its full potential. Wherever wheat grows poorly, triticale may succeed and produce a tasty food grain profitably.

Although the plant is different from wheat, it has the advantage in that it is not very different. It can be produced by wheat growers with little change in production methods or machinery. However, the government price-support programs could become a constraint to expanded acreage. Since triticale is not counted as a food-grain crop, farmers switching acreage to it may lose "base acres" under the wheat and small grains commodity programs. Farmers choosing to experiment with triticale also will face price uncertainties, and will not, at least initially, have access to federally subsidized crop insurance and disaster relief. While grain farmers with extra land not now enrolled in government programs can grow triticale without being penalized for exceeding existing acreage bases, there is relatively little such land suitable for small-grain production in many of the nation's most intensively farmed regions.

Prices paid for triticale grain have been low in recent years because it has sold mainly as a feed grain. Not only is this the lowest price market, but the levels have been determined by the prices of corn and soybean, both of which have been depressed. With the market's apparent rebound in the late 1980s, it seems reasonable to assume that triticale will become more attractive in the future than in the past.

FOOD USES

Although triticale has potential for use in the American food industry, it is far from being a reality. Wheat, the nation's established breadmaking cereal, has been in surplus for over a decade, making it nearly impossible for any new cereal to make deep inroads into breadmaking. Today, some triticales are used as taste-enhancing additives to specialty breads and baked goods, but, in the absence of sizable and stable markets, the crop has so far attracted little interest from the national food industry.

Nonetheless, many food uses could develop in the future. Triticale adds flavor to cookies, crackers, and breads. It has a taste that many people like instantly. New varieties have much better breadmaking qualities than those of the past—although they do have the "sticky dough" problem (see chapter 4). In the case of large industrial bakeries, this problem currently limits the use of triticale to blends with wheat flour.

FEED USES

In the United States at this point, triticale is most popular as a forage and feed grain. For this purpose, it is particularly valuable to farmers who want to grow their own feed. Also, its high lysine content means that farmers can save on purchases of supplemental protein. In places (such as the Southeast and Northwest) that are distant from the soybean-growing area in the Midwest, this could be a valuable saving.

Because grain sold for animal feed is less valuable than the same grain sold for human consumption, triticale has to yield at least 15 percent more than wheat to be profitable for a farmer. On poor soils in several parts of the nation, it is proving it can do this. In yield trials, winter triticales have actually produced far more per acre than barley, rye, and oats. In one set of trials, for instance, yields were 2,186 lb per acre at Comfort, Texas, and 4,810 lb per acre in an irrigation trial at Garden City, Kansas. The barley checks produced 1,173 lb per acre and 4,581 lb per acre, respectively.[2]

Triticale grain has the nutritional quality to be an excellent feed. In pig-feeding trials, it was shown to be just as palatable as wheat and corn, and has been fed ad libitum without problem.[3] It gave growth performance comparable to that of traditional feed grains.

Triticale is also attractive for feeding poultry. Trials on quail, chickens, broiler turkeys, and tom (male) turkeys have all been successful. In Oregon, variety Flora has been fed to tom turkeys without adversely affecting semen production. When the meat quality was tested, the toms fed exclusively on triticale had significantly improved meat tenderness. Triticale has also been fed to broiler breeder males without causing loss of semen or other qualities.[4]

In North Dakota, an awnless type has been released for forage use.[5]

THE SOUTHEAST

The crop is now establishing itself in the Southeast, where it is grown to a small but increasing extent for winter grazing and for spring feed-grain supply. The region is deficient in feed grains—barley and grain sorghum grow poorly there. Triticale is proving that it can neatly fill a specific market niche. Produced as a winter crop, it is harvested

[2] Metzger, 1974.
[3] Information from R. Myer.
[4] Information from D. T. Savage.
[5] Information from F. Cholick.

in early spring, a time when feed grains are scarce. It comes in three months before the corn crop, for instance.[6]

Some Florida researchers now see triticale as a southern counterpart of barley in the western states and the Dakotas, where wheat and barley are grown side by side. Despite wheat's greater value, barley maintains its niche because it is high yielding, flexible, and grows well on poor soils. Triticale has the same potential qualities, and thus it, too, deserves consideration even where wheat or other crops appear to be more profitable.

The University of Florida has released two triticale varieties. One, FL–201, was grown on 10,000 acres in 1988. The other, Florico, developed as a summer crop for Minnesota, is proving valuable as a winter crop across the deep South. Both FL–201 and Florico give high grain yields—as high as those of wheat on the lower coastal plains where yields of 60–70 bushels per acre are common. As a result, there is rising interest among local farm communities—only the availability of seed is holding back triticale's rapid expansion as a crop for the Southeast.

An important advantage is that the crop fits into multiple cropping systems. It can, for instance, be grown in an annual rotation with soybeans, grain sorghum, beans, corn, or other vegetables. Plots at Quincy, Florida, have yielded the equivalent of 94 bushels of triticale and 45 bushels of soybeans per acre on the same land in the same year. Such combinations can be used to help manage land intensively—allowing farmers to keep a crop in the ground year-round.[7]

THE MIDWEST

Triticale's built-in resilience to drought, toxic soils, and other adversity may give it a new life in the wheat belt, where the possibility of changing climate and rising soil acidity are increasing concerns.

The drought of 1988 brought home to millions the warming trend that seems to be occurring across the farm belt. But what is less well known is that in states such as Kansas, Nebraska, and Oklahoma, surface soils are dropping towards pH 5, thereby creating aluminum and manganese toxicity in crops such as wheat. This acidification seems to result from the decades-long use of nitrogen fertilizers. Although surface soils can be de-acidified with lime, this is expensive and not always practical.

---

[6] Information from R. Barnett.

[7] Information in this section from R. Myer and R. Barnett (see Research Contacts).

Where either surface or subsoils are acidified, triticale's outstanding tolerance to acidity, aluminum, and manganese may give it an edge. It has more aluminum tolerance than even the most tolerant wheats. Its benefits may come in better yields, reduced lime requirements, improved water use, better avoidance of drought, or increased resistance to pests.

Research in Wisconsin has shown that triticale may have unique usefulness as a cover crop.[8] Its many robust characteristics make it good for protecting land from erosion. Moreover, it gives such thick ground cover that it shades weeds and reduces the need for herbicides. These are increasingly valuable traits, given the growing interest in the use of cover crops on set-aside acres and in low-input agriculture systems. Triticale's high forage yields and palatability to livestock offer intriguing prospects for its inclusion in multi-year rotations involving corn, soybeans, triticale, and hay. Because of its drought hardiness, the plant may emerge as a particularly valuable rotational crop in arid regions of the country shifting from excessively high-cost irrigation-based production systems to dryland rotations.

THE NORTHWEST

In Oregon, Washington, and Idaho, winter triticale is attracting attention because it yields better than wheat on upland plateaus.[9] Moreover, in places such as Oregon's Willamette Valley, it is finding a specialty niche because it tolerates alkaline soils that wheat cannot. Also, as noted above, triticale's lysine is a commercial advantage because soybeans have to be imported long distances to feed the local livestock.

Most interest in the crop is now in feeding poultry, horses, and hogs. It is seen as a potential replacement for oats, which are sometimes difficult to find and are expensive in the Northwest. Dozens of small farmers in Idaho are growing triticale to feed hogs. For this purpose it works well. It is easy to raise, and the farmers can use their own crop to feed their own animals.

The state of Oregon has released a semidwarf winter type called "Flora." This is a high-yielding type[10] for growing on the alkaline soils in eastern Oregon, above 3,500 feet. Unfortunately, it produces shriveled grains and is a little late maturing.[11] Nonetheless, it is being

[8] Information from M. Brinkman.
[9] Information from M. Kolding.
[10] Based on Bokolo (Tom Thumb), a variety developed in Hungary by A. Kiss.
[11] Oregon's hot, dry summer days contribute to triticale's sterility and shrunken kernels and also accentuate shattering caused by the weak rachis on some lines.

grown as a replacement for wheat on set-aside land and in alkaline-soil areas (notably in the La Grande area and to its south) where neither wheat nor barley produces acceptable yields.

Triticales in Oregon have exhibited variable response to major diseases such as rust, bunt, snow mold, and barley-yellow-dwarf virus. The lines tested also have responded variably to aluminum concentrations, frost heaving, winter freezing, and wet soils. The short-statured triticales withstand the wind and water loads common to the irrigated cropland along the Columbia River.

One thing has had some area growers concerned: the fear that this "son of rye" may become a weed in their future crops. However, triticale has never shown evidence of reverting to its parents. And, although it has many rustic qualities, it is more like wheat than rye as far as reseeding goes. Thus, seeds dropped in the fields seem unlikely to cause severe weed problems in later crops.

Appendix B

References

A complete and regularly updated bibliography on triticale, written by researchers at the Centro International de Mejoramiento de Maíz y Trigo (CIMMYT) is available. It lists more than 150 titles and covers conventional published literature as well as unconventional reports, studies, and conference proceedings. Photocopies of the individual papers listed in the bibliography are available on request. Requests should be sent to: Scientific Information Unit, CIMMYT, Apartado Postal 6–641, 06600 Mexico, D.F. Photocopies cost US$.10 per page for Latin America (MN$25.00 in Mexico) and US$.20 per page for all other countries.

The rest of this appendix lists articles of general interest that lead deeper into the subject of triticale as well as citations for the papers footnoted throughout the report.

Amaya, A. and B. Skovmand. 1985. Current status of hexaploid triticale quality. Pages 603–606 in *Genetics and Breeding of Triticale: Proceedings of the Third Eucarpia Meeting of the Cereal Section on Triticale, Clermont-Ferrand (France), 2–5 July 1984*. Institut National de la Recherche Agronomique, Paris.

Batterham, E.S. 1986. Nutritional value of triticale for the feeding of livestock. Pages 495–501 in *Proceedings of International Triticale Symposium, Sydney, 1986*. Occasional Publication No. 24, Australian Institute of Agricultural Science, Sydney, Australia.

Bertrand, J.E. and L.S. Dunavin. 1974. Triticale, alone and in a mixture, for grazing by growing beef calves. *Proceedings of Soil Crop Science Society of Florida* 33:48–50.

Bishnoi, U.R. and G.A. Patel. 1979. Comparative yield performance and digestibility of triticale (cultivars) and other small grain forages (rye, wheat, oats, and barley). *Wheat Information Service* (50):41–44. Wheat Information Service, Kihara Institute for Biological Research, Yokohama, Japan.

Bishnoi, U.R., I. Chitapong, I. Hughes, and J. Nishimuta. 1978. Quantity and quality of triticale and other small grain silage. *Agronomy Journal* 70:439–441.

Bragg, D.B. and T.F. Sharby. 1970. Nutritive value of triticale for broiler chick diets. *Poultry Science* 49:1022.

Cicin, N.V. 1972. Die entfernte Hybridisierung von Gramineen (Prozesse der Formenbildung und Methoden zur Uberwindung der Sterilitat); [Distant hybridization of gramineous plants (process of form development and methods to overcome sterility)]. *Deutsche Akademie der Landwirtschaftswissenschaft Tagungsbericht* 120:13–28.

CIMMYT. 1986. *Spring Triticale. Names; Parentage; Pedigrees; Origins*. Compiled by O.S. Abdalla, G. Varughese, E.E. Saari, and H. Braun. CIMMYT, Mexico.

CIMMYT. 1985. Industrial quality of hexaploid triticale. Pages 66–73 in *CIMMYT Research Highlights 1984*. CIMMYT, Mexico.

CIMMYT. 1985. Triticale—a crop for marginal environments. Pages 72–80 in *CIMMYT Research Highlights 1985*. CIMMYT, Mexico

Clark, R.B. 1982. Plant response to mineral element toxicity and deficiency. Page 80 in *Breeding Plants for Less Favorable Environments*, edited by M.N. Christiansen and C.F. Lewis. John Wiley and Sons, Inc., Toronto, Canada.

Cooper, K.V. 1985. *The Australian Triticale Cookery Book*. Savvas Publishing, Adelaide, South Australia.

Darvey, N.L., ed. 1986. *Proceedings of International Triticale Symposium, Sydney, 1986*. Occasional Publication No. 24, Australian Institute of Agricultural Science, Sydney, Australia.

Davis, R.L. and B.C. Radcliffe. 1984. Performance of growing pigs fed wheat, barley or triticale. *Australian Journal of Experimental Agriculture and Animal Husbandry* 24:501–506.

Erickson, J.P., E.R. Miller, F.C. Elliot, P.K. Ku, and D.E. Ullrey. 1979. Nutritional evaluation of triticale in swine starter and grower diets. *Journal of Animal Science* 48:547–553.

European Association for Research on Plant Breeding. 1985. *Genetics and Breeding of Triticale: Proceedings of the Third Eucarpia Meeting of the Cereal Section on Triticale, Clermont-Ferrand (France), 2–5 July 1984*. Institut National de la Recherche Agronomique, Paris.

Farrell, D.J., C.C. Chan, and F. McCrae. 1983. A nutritional evaluation of triticale with pigs. *Animal Feed Science Technology* 9:49–62.

Forsberg, R.A., editor. 1985. *Triticale*. Crop Science Society of America Special Publication No. 9. American Society of Agronomy, Madison, Wisconsin, USA.

Gill, K.S. 1986. Current status and future prospects of breeding triticale. Pages 84–104 in *Proceedings of International Triticale Symposium, Sydney, 1986*. Occasional Publication No. 24, Australian Institute of Agricultural Science, Sydney, Australia.

Gupta, P.K. and P.M. Priyadarshan. 1982. Triticale: present status and future prospects. *Advances in Genetics* 21:255–345.

Gustafson, J.P. 1983. Cytogenetics of triticale. Pages 225–250 in *Cytogenetics of Crop Plants*, edited by M.S. Swaminathan, P.K. Gupta, and U. Sinha. New York, Macmillan.

Hulse, J.H. and E.M. Laing. 1974. *Nutritive Value of Triticale Protein*. International Development Research Centre, IDRC–021e, Ottawa, Canada.

Institut Technique des Céréales et des Fourrages (ITCF). 1985. *Triticale: Culture et Utilisation*. ITCF, Paris, France.

Islam, A.K.M.R. and K.W. Shepherd. 1980. Meiotic restitution in wheat-barley hybrids. *Chromosoma* (Berlin) 79:363–372.

Johnson, R.J. 1986. The digestibility of nitrogen and amino acids in triticale grain by meat-type poultry. Pages 502–506 in *Proceedings of International Triticale Symposium, Sydney, 1986*. Occasional Publication No. 24, Australian Institute of Agricultural Science, Sydney, Australia.

Khan, A.M. and B.O. Eggum. 1979. The nutritional quality of some Pakistani wheat varieties. *Journal of the Science of Food and Agriculture* 30:779–784.

Lorenz, K. and R.J. Welsh. 1974. In *Triticale: First Man-Made Cereal*, edited by C.C. Tsen. American Association of Cereal Chemists, St. Paul, Minnesota.

Lorenz, K., R.J. Welsh, R. Normann, G. Beetner, and A. Frey. Extrusion processing of triticale. *Journal of Food Science* 39(3):572–576.

Lorenz, K., F.W. Reuter, and C. Sizar. 1976. The mineral composition of triticales and triticale milling fractions by X-ray fluorescence and atomic absorption. *Cereal Chemistry* 51:534–542.

Lukaszewski, A.J. and J.P. Gustafson. 1984. The effect of rye chromosomes on heading date triticale x wheat hybrids. *Zeitschrift für Pflanzenzüchtung* 93:246–250.

McGinnis, J. 1972. Report to Rockefeller Foundation and CIMMYT. Department of Animal Science, Washington State University, Pullman, Washington 99163, USA.

Metzger, R.J. 1974. Triticale: its potential as a cereal crop in the United States. Pages 75–80 in *Triticale: Proceedings of an International Symposium, El Batan, Mexico, 1–3 October 1973*, edited by R. MacIntyre and M. Campbell. International Development Research Centre, IDRC–024e, Ottawa, Canada.

Michela, P. and K. Lorenz. 1976. The vitamins of triticale, wheat, and rye. *Cereal Chemistry* 53:853–861.

Moody, E.G. 1973. Triticale in dairy cattle rations. *Feedstuffs* 45(8):38.

Morris, R. and E.R. Sears. 1987. The cytogenetics of wheat and its relatives. Pages 19–87 in *Wheat and Wheat Improvement*, edited by K.S. Quinsberry and L.P. Reitz. Second edition. Monograph Number 13, American Society of Agronomy, Madison, Wisconsin.

Müntzing, A. 1979. Triticale: results and problems. *Advances in Plant Breeding*, Supplement No. 10 to *Journal of Plant Breeding*. Verlag Paul Parey, Berlin and Hamburg, Federal Republic of Germany.

Myer, R.O. and Barnett, R.D. 1985. Triticale ('Beagle 82') as an energy and protein source in diets for starting growing-finishing swine. *Nutrition Reports International* 31:181–190.

Peña, R.J. and G.M. Ballance. 1987. Comparision of gluten quality in triticale: fractional reconstitution study. *Cereal Chemistry* 64:128–132.

Planchon, C. 1985. Photosynthesis, transpiration, resistance to CO_2 transfer, and water efficiency of flag leaf of bread wheat, durum wheat and triticale. *Euphytica* 28(2):403–408.

Rossi, L. 1978. In *Technology for Increasing Food Production*, edited by J.C. Holmes. FAO, Rome

Saari, E., G. Varughese, and O.S. Abdalla. 1986. Triticale diseases: distribution and importance. Pages 208–231 in *Proceedings of International Triticale Symposium, Sydney, 1986*. Occasional Publication No. 24, Australian Institute of Agricultural Science, Sydney, Australia.

Sekhon, K.S., K.S. Gill, A.K. Saxena, and G.S. Sandha. 1980a. Studies on the bread, cookie and *chapati* making properties of some high yielding varieties of triticale. Pages 178–186 in *Proceedings of Wheat and Your Needs*. New Delhi, India.

Sekhon, K.S., A.K. Saxena, S.K. Randhawa, and K.S. Gill. 1980b. Use of triticale for bread, cookie and *chapati* making. *Journal of Food Science Technology* 17:233–235.

Shimada, A., T.R. Cline, and J.C. Rogler. 1974. Nutritive value of triticale for the nonruminant. *Journal of Animal Science* 38:935–940.

Skovmand, B., P.N. Fox, and R.L. Villareal. 1984. Triticale in commercial agriculture: progress and promise. *Advances in Agronomy* 37:1–45.

Skovmand, B., H.J. Braun, and P.N. Fox. 1985. Comparison of agronomic and quality characteristics of complete and substituted hexaploid spring triticale. Pages 29–34 in *Genetics and Breeding of Triticale: Proceedings of the Third Eucarpia Meeting of the Cereal Section on Triticale, Clermont-Ferrand (France), 2–5 July 1984*. Institut National de la Recherche Agronomique, Paris.

Suijs, L.W. 1986. Le triticale aux Pays-Bas, Allemagne Fédérale, Royaume Uni et le Pays de Gallesc. In *Triticale: International Colloquium*. Ghent, Belgium, Industriële Hogeschool van het Rijk C.T.L.

Taverner, M.R. 1986. The digestibility by pigs of amino acids in triticale, wheat and rye. Pages 507–510 in *Proceedings of International Triticale Symposium, Sydney, 1986*. Occasional Publication No. 24, Australian Institute of Agricultural Science, Sydney, Australia.

Taverner, M.R., I.D. Hume, and D.J. Farrell. 1981. Availability to pigs of amino acids in cereal grains. 1. Endogenous levels of amino acids in ileal digesta and faeces of pigs given cereal diets. *British Journal of Nutrition* 46(1):149–159.

Taverner, M.R., I.D. Hume, and D.J. Farrell. 1981. Availability to pigs of amino acids in cereal grains. 2. Apparent and true ileal availability. *British Journal of Nutrition* 46(1):159–171.

Tschermak, E. and H. Bleier. 1926. Über fruchtbare Aegilops-Weizenbastarde. (Beispiele für die Entstehung neuer Arten durch Bastardierung.) [Fertile Aegilops-wheat hybrids. (Examples of the origin of a new species by hybridzation.)] *Berichte der Deutschen Botanischen Gesellschaft* 44(2):110–132.

Tsitsin, N.V. 1960. *Wide Hybridization in Plants*. Pages 1–30, English translation by Israel Program for Scientific Translations, 1962.

Unrau, A.M. and B.S. Jenkins. 1964. Investigations on synthetic cereal species. Milling, baking and some compositional characteristics of some triticale and parental species. *Cereal Chemistry* 41(5):365–375.

Varughese, G. 1986. Triticale—a crop for marginal environments. Pages 72–80 in *CIMMYT Research Highlights 1985*. CIMMYT, Mexico.

Varughese, G., E.E. Saari, and O.S. Abdalla. 1986. Two decades of triticale breeding and research at CIMMYT. Pages 148–169 in *Proceedings of International Triticale Symposium, Sydney, 1986*. Occasional Publication No. 24, Australian Institute of Agricultural Science, Sydney, Australia.

Varughese, G., T. Barker, and E. Saari. 1987. *Triticale*. CIMMYT, Mexico, D.F.

Villegas, E., B.O. Eggum, S.K. Vasal, and M.M. Kohli. 1980. Progress in nutritional improvement of maize and triticale. *Food and Nutrition Bulletin* 2(1):17–24.

Wu, Y.V., A.C. Stringfellow, R.A. Anderson, K.R. Sexson, and J.S. Wall. 1978. Triticale for food uses. *Journal of Agricultural Food Chemistry* 26:1039–1048.

Zillinsky, F.J. 1973. Triticale breeding and research at CIMMYT: a progress report. *CIMMYT Research Bulletin* 24:74–84. CIMMYT, Mexico.

Zillinsky, F.J. 1974. The development of triticale. *Advances in Agronomy* 26:315–349.

Zillinsky, F.J. 1985. Triticale: an update on yield, adaptation, and world production. Pages 1–7 in *Triticale*. CSSA Special Publication No. 9. Madison, Wisconsin, USA, Crop Science Society of America.

Zillinsky, F.J. and N.E. Borlaug. 1971. Progress in developing triticale as an economic crop. *CIMMYT Research Bulletin* 17:1–27. CIMMYT, Mexico.

Appendix C

Research Contacts

The main body of triticale experience described in this book is currently at CIMMYT, whose address is Lisboa 27, Apartado Postal 6–641, 06600 Mexico, D.F., Mexico. Individual researchers with specific triticale expertise include the following:

Osman Abdalla
Arnoldo Amaya C.
Roberto Javier Peña B.
Paul Fox
Lucy Gilchrist S.
Wolfgang H. Pfeiffer
Bent Skovmand
Enrique Torres
George Varughese

There is, however, a wealth of experience with triticale in countries outside Mexico, including the following:

Paraguay

CIMMYT, C-C 1170, Ascuncion (Pat Wall, Mohan Kohli)

Turkey

CIMMYT, PK 39 Emek, Ankara (Byrd Curtis, Gene Saari, H. J. Brown)

Argentina

Saniago Garbini, INTA, Estación Experimental Agrícola, Bordenave Bayary

Australia

E.S. Batterham, North Coast Agricultural Institute, Wollongbar, New South Wales 2480

Department of Agricultural Genetics and Biometry, The University of Sydney, New South Wales 2006 (Norman L. Darvey, T.P. Angus, G.J. Gale, R.M. Trethowan, B.J. Sutton, F.W. Ellison)

Department of Agriculture and Rural Affairs, Animal Research Institute, Werribee, Victoria 3300 (R.J. Johnson, M.R. Taverner)

Department of Agronomy, Waite Agricultural Institute, University of Adelaide, Glen Osmond, South Australia 5064 (Katharine V. Cooper, D.R. Marshall, Ian Dundas, Robin Graham, Kenneth Shepherd)

Department of Agronomy and Soil Science, University of New England, Armidale, New South Wales 2351 (G.C. Sweenye, H.C. Harris, R.S. Jessop, P.W. Sale, P. Tremain, C. Hill, R. Wright, E. Matheson)

C. Joannides, Victorian Crops Research Institute, Horsham, Victoria 3400
C.E. May, N.S.W. Department of Agriculture, Agricultural Research Institute, Wagga Wagga, New South Wales 2650
R. McIntosh, University of Sydney Plant Breeding Institute, P.O. Box 180, Castle Hill, New South Wales 2154
R. McLean, Western Australia Department of Agriculture, Baron-Hay Court, South Perth, Western Australia 6151
Geoffrey Smart, Pacific Seeds, P.O. Box 337, Toowoomba, Queensland 4350

Bolivia

Oscar Flores Sandoval, Casilla de Correo No. 1153, La Paz
Luis Pierola M., Casilla 3161, Cochabamba
Casiano Quintana Carvajal, Centro Internacional de Agricultura Trópico (CIAT), Av. Ejercito 131, Casilla 247, Santa Cruz

Brazil

CNPT/EMBRAPA, Caixa Postal 569, 99100, Passo Fundo, Rio Grande do Sul (Augusto Carlos Baier, J.L. Nedel)

Bulgaria

Institute of Genetics, Sofia 1113, (Zdravka Sabeva, Pravda Balevska, Irina Vassileva)
Iliya Stankov, Institute of Introduction and Plant Genetic Resources, 4122, Sadovo, Plovdiv District
Stoyan Tsvetkov, Institute of Wheat and Sunflower, 9500 General Toshevo, Tolbuhin

Canada

Alberta Agriculture, Field Crops Branch, 5718–56 Avenue, Bag Service #47, Lacombe, Alberta T0C 1S0 (James Helm, Don Salmon)
W. Bushuk, c/o St. Paul's College, University of Manitoba, Winnipeg, Manitoba R3T 2N2
George Fedak, Cytogenetics Section, Research Station, Research Branch, Agriculture Canada, Ottawa, Ontario K1A 0C6
L.A. Hunt, Crop Science Department, University of Guelph, Guelph, Ontario N1G 2W1
Edward N. Larter, Department of Plant Science, University of Manitoba, Winnipeg, Manitoba R3T 2N2
J. Grant McLeod, Agriculture Canada Research Station, P.O. Box 1030, Swift Current, Saskatchewan, S9H 3X2
L. Shebeski, Department of Plant Science, University of Manitoba, Winnipeg, Manitoba R3T 2N2
J.B. Thomas, Agriculture Canada Research Station, Lethbridge, Alberta T1J 4S4
F.J. Zillinsky, 1385 McMahon Avenue, Gloucester, Ontario, K1T 1C2

Chile

E.E. Purque, Facultad de Agronomía, Pontifica Universidad Católica de Chile, Casilla 114-D, Santiago

Colombia

Rodrigo Britto M., CRI Obonuco, Apartado Aereo 339, Pasto
Alvaro Montes Ramirez, Federación Nacional de Cultivadores de Cereales (FENALCE), Apartado Aereo #8694, Bogotá

Ecuador

Cesar Caceres Rueda, Ministerio de Agricultura Yganderia, Av. Amazonas y Eloy Alfaro, 10 Piso
Victor Hugo Cardoso C., Instituto Nacional de Investigaciones Agropecuarias (INIAP), Casilla 340, Quito

Ethiopia

Hailu Gebre-Mariam, P.O. Box 3745, Addis Ababa

Federal Republic of Germany

Tamas Lelley, Institut für Pflanzenbau und Pflanzenzüchtung, Universität Göttingen, Von Siebold Strasse 8, D–3400 Göttingen

Gitta Oettler, Landessaatzuchtanstalt Universität Hohenheim, Postfach 70 05 62, D–7000 Stuttgart 70

L. Seidewitz, Institut für Pflanzenbau und Pflanzenzüchtung (FAL), Bundesallee 50, D–3300 Braunschweig

Federal Research Centre for Cereal and Potato Processing, Detmold (D. Weipert, B. Fretzdorff, K. Seiler)

Jutta Zeddies, Frenke, Am Thie 2, D–3254 Emmerthal 16

Finland

Department of Plant Breeding, University of Helsinki, 00710 Helsinki (P. Ryöppy, P.M.A. Tigerstedt, J. Honkanen)

E. I. Kivi, Hankkija Plant Breeding Institute, SF–04300 Hyrylä

France

Yves Beaux, Laboratoire Institut Technique des Céréales et Fourrages, 16 rue N. Fortin, F–75013 Paris

Semences Cargill, B.P. 17, Boissay, 28390 Toury (Jean-Pierre Jaubertie, Guy Dorlencourt)

J. N. Caron, SOGROUP, Sélection Céréales, 9 rue de Faches, Coutiches, 59310 Orchies

Louis Foret, Agri-Obtentions, B. P. 53, 78193 Trappes Cedex

Institut National de la Recherche Agronomique (INRA), Station d'Amélioration des Plantes, Domaine de Crouelle, 63039 Clermont-Ferrand Cedex (Michel Bernard, Directeur Programme Triticale; Michel Lafarge; Sylvie Bernard; Gilles Charmet)

Institut National de la Recherche Agronomique (INRA), Station de Pathologie Végétale, Centre de Recherches de Versailles, Route de St. Cyr, 78000 F Versailles (Michele Skajennikoff, Frantz Rapilly)

J. P. Josset, Graines Franco Sueduises, Station de Sélection Weibull, Semonville Cedex 1824, 28310 Janville

Michel Lafarge, Institut National de la Recherche Agronomique (INRA), 12 avenue du Brézet, 63039 Clermont-Ferrand

G. Laroche, Institut Technique des Céréales et Fourrages (ITCF), 7 rue Montlosier, 63000 Clermont-Ferrand

Jean Paul Legoff, Société R.A.G.T., 18 rue Séguret Saincric, 12003 Rodez Cedex

German Democratic Republic

R. Schlegel, Zentralinstitut für Genetik und Kulturpflanzenforschung, Akademie der Wissenschaften der DDR, DDR-4325 Gatersleben, Corrensstrasse 3

A. Winkel, Institut für Pflanzenzüchtung, Akademie der Landwirtschaftswissenschaften der DDR Republik, 2601 Gülzow

Greece

Pantousis J. Kaltsikes, The Athens School of Agricultural Sciences, Iera Odos 75, 118 55, Athens

India

Department of Plant Breeding, Punjab Agricultural University, Ludhiana 141 004 (Khem Singh Gill, R.K. Vellanki, G.S. Sandha, G.S. Dhindsa, A. Nityagopal, G.S. Nanda)

P.K. Gupta, Department of Agricultural Botany, Meerut University, Meerut

A. Ramachandra Reddy, Department of Botany, Sri Venkateswara University, Tirupati, District Chittoor, Andhra Pradesh 517 502

G.M. Reddy, Department of Genetics, Osmania University, Hyderabad

Italy

ENEA-C.R.E. Casaccia, Biologiche ed Agrarie-Dip. TECAB, S.P., Anguillarese Km 1.300, 00100 Rome (Luigi Rossi, B. Giorgi)
Leto Impiglia, Cereals Programme for Africa, Crop and Grassland Production Service, Plant Production and Protection Division, F.A.O., Via delle Terme di Caracalla, 00100 Rome

Japan

Faculty of Agriculture, Tottori University, Tottori 680 (M. Sasaki, S. Muraoka, N. Nakata, Y. Yasumuro)
Kazuyoshi Natori, Experimental Farm, Kyoto University, Takatsuki, Osaka, 569
Shoji Shigenaga, Faculty of Agriculture, Kyoto University, Kyoto, 606

Madagascar

M. Rakotondramanana, Fifamanor, P.O. Box 198, Antsirabe 110

Netherlands

CEBECO, Plant Breeding Station, Lisdoddeweg 36, 8219 PR Lelystad
Department of Genetics, Agricultural University, General Foulkesweg 53, 6703 BM Wageningen (J. Sybenga, J. H. de Jong)
Foundation for Agricultural Plant Breeding, P.O. Box 117, 6700 AC Wageningen
Lock W. Sus, Geertsema Zaden BV, NL–9700 AK Groningen

Norway

Jon Mjaerum, Department of Crop Science, Box 41, N–1432 AAS-NLH

Pakistan

Nuclear Institute for Agriculture and Biology, Faisalabad (M. Siddique Sadiq, M. Saleem, Javed Iqbal)

People's Republic of China

Wen-Kui Bao, Chinese Academy of Agricultural Sciences, Beijing

Peru

René Romero Davalos, Avenida Sol-Pasaje Grace-Edif. San Jorge, 4to piso F., Cuzco
Anibal Tamayo E., San Miguel #240, Cuzco

Poland

Zofia Banaszak, Poznan Plant Breeders, Plant Breeding Station, Danków 05–620 Bredów
Lidia Bmykryviska, Poznan Plant Breeders, Plant Breeding Station, Danków, 05–620 Bredów
L. Grochowski, Experimental Breeding Station, 63–743 Smolice
Teresa Huskowska, Plant Breeding Station, LASKI, 05–660 Warka
B. Lapinski, Plant Breeding and Acclimatization Station "Malyszyn," ul. Szczecinska 15, 66–400 Gorzów Wlkp.
Plant Breeding Institute, Radzików, P.O. Box 1019, 00–950 Warsaw (Andrzej Aniol, Wladyslaw Sowa, Maria Rakowska, Danuta Boros)
Miroslaw Pojmaj, Poznan Plant Breeders, Plant Breeding Station, Danków 05–620 Bredów
Ewa Sawicka, Laboratory of Genetics and Mutagenesis, Botanical Garden, Polish Academy of Sciences, W. Pravdziwka 2, P.O. Box 84, 02–973 Warsaw
Andrzej Szotkowski, SHR Choryn, 64–005 Racot
Ryszard Szymczyk, The Research Center for Cultivars Testing, 63–022 Slupia Wielka
Czeslaw Tarkowski, Instytut Genetyki i Hodowli, Akademia Rolnicza, 20–934 Lublin, ul. Akademicka 15
Tadeusz Wolski, Poznanska Hodowla Roslin, Wspolna 30, 00–930 Warsaw

Portugal

Francisco Bagulho, National Plant Breeding Station, 7351 Elvas Codex
Manuel Barradas, Director, National Station for Plant Breeding, P–7350 Elvas Codex
T. Mello-Sampayo, Instituto Gulbenkian de Ciencia, Apartado 14, 2781 Oeiras Codex
Universidade de Trás-os-Môntes e Alto Douro, 5000 Vila Real (Divisão de Genética e Melhoramento de Plantas, H. Guedes-Pinto, Head; Divisão de Nutrição Animal, A. Dias-da-Silva, A. Mascarenhas Ferreira; Dep. Economia e Sociologia, J.F.G. Portela; Divisão de Solos e Fertilidade, Ester Portela, Joao F. Coutinho; Departamento de Geociências, A.L. Pires, Departamento de Fitotecnia, Carlos A.B.B. Castro)

Spain

Departamento de Genética Agraria, Escuela T.S. Ingenieros Agrónomos, Ciudad Universitaria, 28040 Madrid (Enrique Sanchez-Monge y Parellada, José Maria Carillo Becerril)
Institut d'Investigació i Desenvolupament Agrari, 25006 Lérida (J.A. Martin Sanchez, I. Romagosa)
Nicolas Jouve, Director del Departmento de Biologia Celular y Genetica, Universidad de Alcala de Henares, Apartado 20, Alcala de Henares, Madrid
Ramon Giraldez, Departmento de Biologia Funcional, Universidad de Oviedo, Oviedo

Sweden

Arnulf Merker, Svalöf AB, S–26800 Svalöv

Switzerland

Swiss Federal Research Station for Agriculture, CH–1260 Nyon (G. Kleijer, gene bank; A. Fossati, breeding department)

Tunisia

Institut National de la Recherche Agronomique de Tunisie (INRAT), Ave de l'Indépendance, Ariana 2080 (M. Lassram, Director; B. Salem, food value and technology use; R. A. Maamouri, triticale improvement)
Bergaoui Ridha, Ecole Supérieure d'Agriculture, 7030 Mateur

Turkey

Macit Ulubelde, Director, The Library, Regional Agricultural Research Institute, P.O. Box 9, Menemen-Izmir

United Kingdom

Plant Breeding Institute, Maris Lane, Trumpington, Cambridge CB2 2LQ, England (R.S. Gregory, P.J. Webb, P.R. Hampson, R.A. Kempton)
M. R. Ward, Asmer Seed Company, 1500 Melton Road, Queniborough, Leicester LE7 8FN, England

Union of Soviet Socialist Republics

A.A. Sozinov, N.I. Vavilov Institute of General Genetics, USSR Academy of Sciences, Moscow
Triticale Laboratory, V. Y. Yuryev Ukrainian Research Institute of Plant Production, Breeding and Genetics, 142, Moskovsky prospekt, Kharkov, 310060 (Grigori Gorban)

United States of America

Thomas Barker, Cornell University, Ithaca, New York 14853
Ronald Barnett, North Florida Research and Education Center, University of Florida, 3, Box 4370, Quincy, Florida 32351
Marshall Brinkman, Department of Agronomy, University of Wisconsin, Madison, Wisconsin 53706

Philip Bruckner, U.S. Department of Agriculture, Agricultural Research Service, Tifton, Georgia 31793
Robert Busch, Department of Agronomy, University of Minnesota, St. Paul, Minnesota 55108
Fred Cholick, Department of Plant Science, South Dakota State University, Box 2230, Brookings, South Dakota 57007
Fred C. Elliott, 1084 Angus Way, Yuma, Arizona 85364
Emanuel Epstein, Department of Land, Air and Water Resources, Hoagland Hall, University of California, Davis, California 95616
Bikram Gill, Professor, Department of Plant Pathology, Throckmorton Hall, Kansas State University, Manhattan, Kansas 66506
J.P. Gustafson, Department of Agronomy, University of Missouri, Columbia, Missouri 65211
Robert G. Hall, Department of Plant Science, South Dakota State University, Box 2230, Brookings, South Dakota 57007
Charles Hayward, Pioneer International Hybrid Seed Company, Hutchinson, Kansas
Charles Jenkins, 418A Cayuga Street, Salinas, California 93901
A.R. Klatt, Assistant Dean, International Programs, Oklahoma State University, Stillwater, Oklahoma 74078
Mathias Kolding, Cereal Breeder, Columbia Basin Research Center, P.O. Box 105, Hermiston, Oregon 97838
Klaus Lorenz, Department of Food Science and Human Nutrition, Colorado State University, Fort Collins, Colorado 80523
Adam J. Lukaszewski, Department of Agronomy, University of Missouri, Columbia, Missouri 65211
Milton E. McDaniel, Department of Soil and Crop Science, Texas A&M University, College Station, Texas 77843
James McGinnis, Department of Animal Science, Washington State University, Pullman, Washington 99164
Robert J. Metzger, 2838 N.W. 29th, Corvallis, Oregon 97330
Darrell D. Morey, Department of Agronomy, University of Georgia, Coastal Plain Experimental Station, Tifton, Georgia 31793
Robert Myer, University of Florida Agricultural Research and Education Center, Route 3, Box 376, Marianna, Florida 32446
Stan Nalepa, Sun/Seeds Genetics, Inc., 9800 Fairview Road, Hollister, California 95023
Clarence J. Peterson, Jr., 209 Johnson Hall, Washington State University, Pullman, Washington 99163
Kenneth Porter, Texas Agricultural Experiment Station, U.S. Department of Agriculture Southwestern Great Plains Research Center, Bushland, Texas 79012
Robert Riestenberg, Lupin-Triticale Enterprise, P.O. Box 187, Perham, Minnesota 56573
V.T. Sapra, Department of Natural Resources and Environmental Studies, Alabama A&M University, Normal, Alabama 35762
D. Thomas Savage, Department of Poultry Science, Dryden Hall, Oregon State University, Corvallis, Oregon 97331–3402
John Schmidt, c/o Agronomy Department, University of Nebraska, Lincoln, Nebraska 68588
R.G. Sears, Agronomy Department, Kansas Sate University, Manhattan, Kansas 66506
Mark Sorrells, Department of Plant Breeding and Biometry, Cornell University, 252 Emerson Hall, Ithaca, New York 14850
James Vetter, America Institute of Baking, 1213 Bakers Way, Manhattan, Kansas 66502

Appendix D

In putting this report together, we came across a remarkable document that, although humorous in outlook, summarizes in large measure the interrelationship of wheat, rye, and triticale that is at the heart of the report. We present it here for general interest.

If Chromosomes Could Speak . . .

by

Henrique Guedes-Pinto and Tristâo Mello-Sampayo[1]

THE TRITICALE MANIFESTO

We belong to the party of the R chromosomes, the chromosomes of rye, that species which has been scorned and considered marginal, relegated for centuries to the poorest soils, the harshest winter conditions, rarely receiving adequate fertilizer.

And all this in favor of wheat, a crop which has been held in high esteem since Biblical times. Man has always given wheat the benefits of the most fertile lands and valleys, the best fertilizers and care, the most up-to-date research and technology, and the highest quotation on the grain market.

The question must be asked: What are the consequences of this elitist situation that rejects rye in favor of wheat?

The consequences are all too clear—monoculture, with self-pollinating plant species, with the consequent risk of rapidly spreading disease and blight; the powerful cereal monopolies (and their accompanying economic and political interests); and, most serious of all, the alarming "genocide" resulting from the continuous impoverishment of genetic variability, that unique treasure trove accumulated by Nature in the course of evolution and now being squandered through the overcultivation of a very few selected genotypes of wheat, pompously designated as "cultivars." This situation has caused the progressive elimination and loss of all other existing and potential genetic combinations.

Rye, as an allogamous plant, takes pride in its role as the preserver of a significant degree of genetic variability, even as it sees its cultivation area further diminished every year.

---

[1] Instituto Universitario de Trás-os-Môntes e Alto Douro, Vila Real, Portugal, April 1985. Translated from *Brotéria-Genética III* (LXXVII), 5–9 (1982).

It is essential that people be informed of this state of affairs immediately. We must put a stop to this elitism once and for all, not only because it is unjust but because it represents a grave danger to the future.

Nevertheless, since it is not our intention to do away with one injustice (the privileged status of wheat) only to replace it with another (extensive monoculture of rye), we propose a united front of all wheat and rye chromosomes in which the chromosomes of both species, working side by side, will be able to participate in the gigantic and heroic task of creating a new cereal: Triticale.

Wheat and rye chromosomes unite! Let us create one common front and banish the old injustices and privileges forever. Let us, with this union of our combined genetic information, build a New Cereal, the Cereal of the Future.

COUNTER MANIFESTO BY THE WHEAT RELATIVES

It was with astonishment and strong displeasure that we, the wheat relatives of the genus *Aegilops*, *Agropyron*, *Elymus*, etc., came upon the pamphlet entitled "The Triticale Manifesto."

In the said document, rye claims that it has been squeezed out, a victim of discrimination by wheat. This is a curious statement indeed from a cereal of great importance during the Middle Ages and one that has always benefited from being an alternative crop for those areas rejected by wheat as unsuited to its temperament.

Even more curious is the fact that rye, in protesting against its relegation to inferior status and denouncing the injustices of the status of wheat, forgot to mention its own kin of the same genus, *Secale vavilovii*, *Secale segetale*, *Secale ancestrale*, etc., species which have indeed been disregarded and sometimes even subjected to persistent elimination from cereal culture altogether.

Even if it could be claimed that rye has been rejected as an important cereal crop, what could then be said of the sorry situation of genera *Aegilops*, *Agropyron*, *Hyanaldia*, etc., which are the real victims of discrimination? It seems that rye is conveniently glossing over a whole gamut of *Triticinae* genera, which once played a fundamental role in the evolution of wheat itself and now find themselves totally ignored and the victims of discrimination.

The situation is all the more despotic and unjust when one considers that they are also legitimate descendants of wheat's ancestors and living repositories of *Triticinae* variability.

Could it be that rye, in speaking of the genetic erosion that wheat suffered and is suffering, forgets that the preservation of genetic variability lies with us, the species designated as "wild wheat" or sometimes "relatives" of wheat?

Was it not from *Triticum dicoccoides* that high-protein grains were obtained and from the *Aegilops ventricosa* that the genes resistant to *Pseudocercosporella herpotrichoides* (eyespot) were taken for wheat, which lacked them or had already lost them? And was it not from the *Aegilops umbellulata*, *Aegilops comosa*, *Agropyron elongatum*, and *Agropyron intermedium* that resistance to rust was taken? How many more resistances and other desirable characteristics can yet be taken from the genetic pools?

Here lies the reason for our denunciation of the false claims uttered by the supporters of rye through their "Triticale Manifesto," which is but another form of elitism in disguise.

It is for this that we launch a new manifesto, not aiming at strict class alliances, but proposing the formation of a new repository of cereals, regardless of their genomic constitution or ploidy level. We work toward a movement in which all cereal chromosomes will be united, not only in one New Cereal (pompously designated "the first man-made cereal") but also in other new cereals besides Triticale such as *Hordecale* (amphidiploid of barley and rye), *Triticordeum* (amphidiploid of wheat and barley) and many more, not scorning any contribution, be it of chromosomes or only a few genes found in countless other gramineous strains, that will prove to be of undeniable value to the betterment of many cereals.

Chromosomes! Let us form a REAL FRONT in the fight for new cereals so that we may, united and independent of ploidy levels or genomic makeup, be victorious in the struggle for a greater and better grain production.

REACTION OF WHEAT

Awake O ye Gods! Woe betide! My sisters, members of the subtribe *Triticinae*, are remonstrating against me with cries of discrimination. And more, they aggravate their deed by slandering none other than myself, whose nobility is above reproach—I, who have done all to further their station, serving as a beacon in their difficult voyage from remote sites of the Near East or the fringe of arid frontiers to the fertile and glorious fields of modern agriculture; I who have twice joined in alliance with my poorer relatives, only to have them complain of my slighting them. The problem goes back to when I, in my original diploid form as *Triticum monococcum* and enjoying comfort and peace in my Fertile Crescent stronghold, started good-neighborly relations with a poor relative, a diploid *Aegilops* of the Sitopsis Section, probably *Aegilops searsii*. Soon, enamored of each other, we joined our genomes (my A with her B), and in this way, duplicating our chromosome complement, we generated an allotetraploid wheat, the wild ancestor of the most noble *durum* wheat of contemporary pasta. Thus joined, we expanded our area to the North until we came upon another diploid relative, the poor and isolated *Aegilops squarrosa*. At my suggestion, there was a new crossing, adding in this manner the genome D to the two already linked. This union proved to be of immeasurable genetic potential, as it enabled the new allohexaploid to generate many other kinds, finally achieving that prodigy of perfection and ubiquity, *Triticum aestivum*, the common bread wheat that we are today.

It was on account of this potential that Man, our true master, was able to isolate, create, and select an untold number of cultivars, which presently encircle the world from end to end in a fraternal and loving embrace, so that we now constitute the staple food of more than 40 countries representing 35 percent of the population of the globe. With his knowledge and ingenuity, our master fashioned these cultivars to fit the requirements of different environments, a feat made possible only by the great capability for variation brought about by our three genomes A, B, and D. Gradually we helped Man settle on the land by guaranteeing him his daily bread. We helped to free him from the darkness and insecurity of nomadic, pastoral life, enabling him to form stable, permanent communities. This new order greatly furthered Man's creativity and the progress of civilization.

In order to reach certain remote areas, we had to travel in the saddlebags and knapsacks of pilgrims, warriors and navigators; we were present at many of History's great moments; we have seen the building of cities, the rise and fall of kingdoms, the beginning and end of empires, the founding of new religions; we have walked alongside many great thinkers, poets, prophets and men of goodwill. Since the earliest civilizations, our bread has been made sacred and, embodying Love and Hope, it has reached the mouths of the humble and starving. We were avariciously kept for millennia in the funerary chambers of powerful kings and lords. Finally, we have arrived at this marvelous but terrifying contemporary civilization, where we are so esteemed and desired.

And do these sisters of mine still doubt my fondness for them? Behold, see how I acceded to an alliance with that outcast of marginal land, *Secale cereale* (rye), in order to generate triticale, without in any way depleting my natural potential for variability. See how I have already made pact with other sisters (species of the genera *Aegilops*, *Agropyron*, *Haynaldia*, etc.), resigning myself to the removal of the Ph suppressors of homeologous chromosomes pairing so that, in the hybrids, my precious chromosomes would readily join with those of my partners in meiosis, facilitating genetic interchange. To them I have conceded the privilege of undergoing gene recombination with me. Furthermore, I have already consented to a private consultation with my distant cousin barley for similar purposes.

I do recognize that thousands of years elapsed between each of my first alliances. Considering my sisters' longevity, however, should they not show more patience in such matters? In any case, the moment has come for them to calm their millennary fears, since genetic engineering is demonstrating new abilities for diverse achievements, both chromosomal and molecular. It is now possible to transfer and to associate in one plant the nascent, I would even venture to say ideal, characteristics of a new cereal in which I will undoubtedly be the predominant element.

Do not forget then, my sisters, that without me you are worth very little, but that I am always at your side to help pull your feet from the mire.

Let us have no more despondency, provocations or threats.

Appendix E

Biographical Sketches of Panel Members

WILLIAM L. BROWN, retired president and chairman of Pioneer Hi-Bred International, received his Ph.D. from Washington University (St. Louis) in 1942. He joined Pioneer in 1945 as a cytogeneticist and did research in maize genetics and breeding until 1965, when he was appointed director of corporate research. He was elected executive vice president in 1973 and president in 1975. He is a member of the National Academy of Sciences and currently serves as chairman of the Board on Agriculture, National Research Council-National Academy of Sciences. Dr. Brown's research has centered around maize genetics and breeding, racial relationships in maize, evolution of North American maize, and conservation and utilization of genetic resources.

RICARDO BRESSANI, head of the Divison of Food and Agricultural Science and research coordinator of the Institute of Nutrition of Central America and Panama (INCAP), Guatemala, received his Ph.D. in biochemistry from Purdue University in 1956; an M.S. from Iowa State University, and a B.S. from the University of Dayton. He has been a member of the professional staff of INCAP since 1956 and visiting professor at the Massachusetts Institute of Technology and Rutgers University in nutrition and food science. His work has dealt with the nutritional quality of basic food crops and human nutrition research. After the discovery of opaque–2 at Purdue, he evaluated samples for nutritional quality using children and demonstrating the exceptional qualities of this type of maize. During his career at INCAP, Dr. Bressani has been involved in the development of high-quality foods such as INCAPARINA, MAISOY, and others; in studying new sources of nutritents; food processing and evaluation; human and animal nutrition; and nutrition-intervention studies. His current work is on amaranth grain and food grain legumes, particularly common beans. He has published many scientific articles and chapters and has edited a number of proceedings of conferences. He is editor of *Archivos Latino-Americanos de Nutrición* and of the *Amaranth Newsletter*. He is a foreign associate of the U. S. National Academy of Sciences, founding member of the Third World Academy of Sciences, and Doctor Honoris causa in Agriculture from Purdue University. Recently he was granted the "Albert Einstein Award" by the World Cultural Council.

DAVID V. GLOVER, professor of plant genetics and breeding, Department of Agronomy, Purdue University, received a B.S. in agronomy in 1954 and an M.S. in plant breeding in 1959 from Utah State University. He received a Ph.D. in Genetics from the University of California, Davis, in 1962, and has served on the faculty at Purdue since that time. His research has centered around the genetics, cytogenetics, physiological genetics, and breeding of maize germplasm with major emphasis on improvement of carbohydrate, protein, and nutritional quality factors. He served as principal investigator and coordinator of the Purdue-U.S. Agency for International Development project on the inheritance and improvement of protein quality and content in maize. He was involved in consultancy activities on protein and nutritional-quality improvement in cereals.

ARNEL R. HALLAUER, research geneticist, USDA/ARS, and professor of agronomy, Iowa State University, Ames, received his Ph.D. from Iowa State University in 1960 and has been stationed at Ames, Iowa, since 1962. His research interests have emphasized basic research of maize relative to quantitative genetics, recurrent selection, and the evaluation and adaptation of exotic germplasm for the U.S. Corn Belt. He has written one book, *Quantitative Genetics in Maize Breeding*, serves as an editor for four journals, and has written numerous articles for scientific journals.

VIRGIL A. JOHNSON was, until recently, leader of wheat research, U.S. Department of Agriculture, and professor, University of Nebraska-Lincoln. He received his Ph.D. degree in plant breeding and genetics from the University of Nebraska in 1952. He coordinates the cooperative state-federal hard red winter wheat program in central United States and supervises an international winter wheat evaluation network in 38 countries. He has been active in numerous international wheat activities. His research has involved the development of improved wheat varieties for the hard red winter wheat regions of the United States and the genetics and physiology of high protein in wheat.

CALVIN O. QUALSET, director of the California Genetic Resources Conservation Program and professor of agronomy at the University of California, received a Ph.D. in Genetics from that institution in

1964. He has served on the faculty at the University of Tennessee and was a department chairman and later associate dean at U.C. Davis during the period 1975–1986. His research area is on the genetics, breeding, and genetic resources of cereal crops, especially focusing on wheat and triticale. He leads a team that has introduced numerous wheat and triticale varieties to California agriculture and has published extensively on the genetics of characters important in adaptation of wheat to specific environments. He has served on several consultancies in developing countries and was a Fulbright Scholar to Australia in 1976 and Yugoslavia in 1984.

NOEL D. VIETMEYER, staff officer and technical writer for this study, is a senior program officer of the Board on Science and Technology for International Development. A New Zealander with a Ph.D. in organic chemistry from the University of California, Berkeley, he now works on innovations in science and technology that are important for the future of developing countries.

ADVISORY COMMITTEE ON TECHNOLOGY INNOVATION

ELMER L. GADEN, JR., Department of Chemical Engineering, University of Virginia, Charlottesville, *Chairman*

Members

RAYMOND C. LOEHR, Director, Environmental Studies Program, Cornell University

CYRUS M. MCKELL, Vice President, Research, Native Plants, Inc., Salt Lake City, Utah

DONALD L. PLUCKNETT, Consultative Group on International Agricultural Research, Washington, D.C.

EUGENE B. SHULTZ, JR., Professor of Engineering and Applied Science, Washington University, St. Louis, Missouri

BOARD ON SCIENCE AND TECHNOLOGY FOR INTERNATIONAL DEVELOPMENT

RALPH H. SMUCKLER, Dean of International Studies and Programs, Michigan State University, East Lansing, *Chairman*

Members

PETER D. BELL, The Edna McConnell Clark Foundation, New York, New York

BARBARA A. BURNS, Manager, Systecon Division, Coopers & Lybrand, Duluth, Georgia

GEORGE T. CURLIN, The Fogarty International Center, The National Institutes of Health, Bethesda, Maryland

DIRK FRANKENBERG, Director, Marine Science Program, University of North Carolina, Chapel Hill

ELLEN L. FROST, Director of Government Programs, Westinghouse Electronic Corporation, Washington, D.C.

CATHRYN GODDARD, President, Atlas Associates, Inc., Washington, D.C.

FREDERICK HORNE, Dean of the College of Science, Oregon State University, Corvallis

Board on Science and Technology for International Development
Publications and Information Services (HA-476E)
Office of International Affairs
National Research Council
2101 Constitution Avenue, N.W.
Washington, D.C. 20418 USA

How to Order BOSTID Reports

BOSTID manages programs with developing countries on behalf of the U.S. National Research Council. Reports published by BOSTID are sponsored in most instances by the U.S. Agency for International Development. They are intended for distribution to readers in developing countries who are affiliated with governmental, educational, or research institutions, and who have professional interest in the subject areas treated by the reports.

BOSTID books are available from selected international distributors. For more efficient and expedient service, please place your order with your local distributor. (See list on back page.) Requestors from areas not yet represented by a distributor should send their orders directly to BOSTID at the above address.

Energy

33. **Alcohol Fuels: Options for Developing Countries.** 1983, 128pp. Examines the potential for the production and utilization of alcohol fuels in developing countries. Includes information on various tropical crops and their conversion to alcohols through both traditional and novel processes. ISBN 0–309–04160–0.

36. **Producer Gas: Another Fuel for Motor Transport.** 1983, 112pp. During World War II Europe and Asia used wood, charcoal, and coal to fuel over a million gasoline and diesel vehicles. However the technology has since been virtually forgotten. This report reviews producer gas and its modern potential. ISBN 0–309–04161–9.

56. **The Diffusion of Biomass Energy Technologies in Developing Countries.** 1984, 120pp. Examines economic, cultural, and political factors that affect the introduction of biomass-based energy technologies in developing countries. It includes information on the opportunities for these technologies as well as conclusions and recommendations for their application. ISBN 0–309–04253–4.

Technology Options

14. **More Water for Arid Lands: Promising Technologies and Research Opportunities.** 1974, 153pp. Outlines little-known but promising technologies to supply and conserve water in arid areas. ISBN 0–309–04151–1.

21. **Making Aquatic Weeds Useful: Some Perspectives for Developing Countries.** 1976, 175pp. Describes ways to exploit aquatic weeds for grazing, and by harvesting and processing for use as compost, animal feed, pulp, paper, and fuel. Also describes utilization for sewage and industrial wastewater. ISBN 0–309–04153-X.

34. **Priorities in Biotechnology Research for International Development: Proceedings of a Workshop.** 1982, 261pp. Report of a workshop organized to examine opportunities for biotechnology research in six areas: 1) vaccines, 2) animal production, 3) monoclonal antibodies, 4) energy, 5) biological nitrogen fixation, and 6) plant cell and tissue culture. ISBN 0–309–04256–9.

61. **Fisheries Technologies for Developing Countries.** 1987, 167pp. Identifies newer technologies in boat building, fishing gear and methods, coastal mariculture, artificial reefs and fish aggregating devices, and processing and preservation of the catch. The emphasis is on practices suitable for artisanal fisheries. ISBN 0–309–04260–7.

Plants

25. **Tropical Legumes: Resources for the Future.** 1979, 331pp. Describes plants of the family Leguminosae, including root crops, pulses, fruits, forages, timber and wood products, ornamentals, and others. ISBN 0–309–04154–6.

37. **Winged Bean: A High Protein Crop for the Tropics.** 1981, 2nd edition, 59pp. An update of BOSTID's 1975 report of this neglected tropical legume. Describes current knowledge of winged bean and its promise. ISBN 0–309–04162–7.

53. **Jojoba: New Crop for Arid Lands.** 1985, 102pp. In the last 10 years, the domestication of jojoba, a little-known North American desert shrub, has been all but completed. This report describes the plant and its promise to provide a unique vegetable oil and many likely industrial uses. ISBN 0–309–04251–8.

63. **Quality-Protein Maize.** 1988, 100pp. Identifies the promise of a nutritious new form of the planet's third largest food crop. Includes chapters on the importance of maize, malnutrition and protein quality, experiences with quality-protein maize (QPM), QPM's potential uses in feed and food, nutritional qualities, genetics, research needs, and limitations. ISBN 0–309–04262–3.

64. **Triticale: A Promising Addition to the World's Cereal Grains.** 1988, approx. 120pp. Outlines the recent transformation of triticale, a hybrid between wheat and rye, into a food crop with much potential for many marginal lands. Includes chapters on triticale's history, nutritional quality, breeding, agronomy, food and feed uses, research needs, and limitations. ISBN 0–309–04263–1.

Innovations in Tropical Forestry

35. **Sowing Forests from the Air.** 1981, 64pp. Describes experiences with establishing forests by sowing tree seed from aircraft. Suggests testing and

development of the techniques for possible use where forest destruction now outpaces reforestation. ISBN 0–309–04257–7.

40. **Firewood Crops: Shrub and Tree Species for Energy Production.** Volume II, 1983, 92pp. Examines the selection of species of woody plants that seem suitable candidates for fuelwood plantations in developing countries. ISBN 0–309–04164–3 (Vol. II).

41. **Mangium and Other Fast-Growing Acacias for the Humid Tropics.** 1983, 63pp. Highlights 10 acacia species that are native to the tropical rain forest of Australasia. That they could become valuable forestry resources elsewhere is suggested by the exceptional performance of *Acacia mangium* in Malaysia. ISBN 0–309–04165–1.

42. **Calliandra: A Versatile Small Tree for the Humid Tropics.** 1983, 56pp. This Latin American shrub is being widely planted by the villagers and government agencies in Indonesia to provide firewood, prevent erosion, provide honey, and feed livestock. ISBN 0–309–04166-X.

43. **Casuarinas: Nitrogen-Fixing Trees for Adverse Sites.** 1983, 118pp. These robust, nitrogen-fixing, Australasian trees could become valuable resources for planting on harsh eroding land to provide fuel and other products. Eighteen species for tropical lowlands and highlands, temperate zones, and semiarid regions are highlighted. ISBN 0–309–04167–8.

52. **Leucaena: Promising Forage and Tree Crop in Developing Countries.** 1984, 2nd edition, 100pp. Describes a multi purpose tree crop of potential value for much of the humid lowland tropics. Leucaena is one of the fastest growing and most useful trees for the tropics. ISBN 0–309–04250-X.

Managing Tropical Animal Resources

32. **The Water Buffalo: New Prospects for an Underutilized Animal.** 1981, 188pp. The water buffalo is performing notably well in recent trials in such unexpected places as the United States, Australia, and Brazil. Report discusses the animal's promise, particularly emphasizing its potential for use outside Asia. ISBN 0–309–04159–7.

44. **Butterfly Farming in Papua New Guinea.** 1983, 36pp. Indigenous butterflies are being reared in Papua New Guinea villages in a formal government program that both provides a cash income in remote rural areas and contributes to the conservation of wildlife and tropical forests. ISBN 0–309–04168–6

45. **Crocodiles as a Resource for the Tropics.** 1983, 60pp. In most parts of the tropics, crocodilian populations are being decimated, but programs in Papua New Guinea and a few other countries demonstrate that, with care, the animals can be raised for profit while protecting the wild populations. ISBN 0–309–04169–4.

46. **Little-Known Asian Animals with a Promising Economic Future.** 1983, 133pp. Describes banteng, madura, mithan, yak, kouprey, babirusa, javan warty pig, and other obscure but possibly globally useful wild and domesticated animals that are indigenous to Asia. ISBN 0–309–04170–8.

Health

49. **Opportunities for the Control of Dracunculiasis.** 1983, 65pp. Dracunculiasis is a parasitic disease that temporarily disables many people in remote, rural areas in Africa, India, and the Middle East. Contains the findings and recommendations of distinguished scientists who were brought together to discuss dracunculiasis as an international health problem. ISBN 0–309–04172–4.

55. **Manpower Needs and Career Opportunities in the Field Aspects of Vector Biology.** 1983, 53pp. Recommends ways to develop and train the manpower necessary to ensure that experts will be available in the future to understand the complex ecological relationships of vectors with human hosts and pathogens that cause such diseases as malaria, dengue fever, filariasis, and schistosomiasis. ISBN 0–309–04252–6.

60. **U.S. Capacity to Address Tropical Infectious Diseases.** 1987, 225pp. Addresses U.S. manpower and institutional capabilities in both the public and private sectors to address tropical infectious disease problems. ISBN 0–309–04259–3.

Resource Management

50. **Environmental Change in the West African Sahel.** 1984, 96pp. Identifies measures to help restore critical ecological processes and thereby increase sustainable production in dryland farming, irrigated agriculture, forestry and fuelwood, and animal husbandry. Provides baseline information for the formulation of environmentally sound projects. ISBN 0–309–04173–2.

51. **Agroforestry in the West African Sahel.** 1984, 86pp. Provides development planners with information regarding traditional agroforestry systems — their relevance to the modern Sahel, their design, social and institutional considerations, problems encountered in the practice of agroforestry, and criteria for the selection of appropriate plant species to be used. ISBN 0–309–04174–0.

General

65. **Science and Technology for Development: Prospects Entering the Twenty-First Century.** 1988. 79pp. This report commemorates the twenty-fifth anniversary of the U.S. Agency for International Development. The symposium on which this report is based provided an excellent opportunity to describe and assess the contributions of science and technology to the development of Third World countries, and to focus attention on what science and technology are likely to accomplish in the decades to come.

Forthcoming Books from BOSTID

Lost Crops of the Andes (1989)

Microlivestock: Little-Known Small Animals with a Promising Economic Future (1989)

Saline Agriculture: Salt-Tolerant Plants for Food, Fuel, Fodder, and Other Products in Developing Countries (1989)

Traditional Fermented Foods (1990)

For More Information

To receive more information about BOSTID reports and programs, please fill in the attached coupon and mail it to:

Board on Science and Technology for International Development
Publications and Information Services (HA–476E)
Office of International Affairs
National Research Council
2101 Constitution Avenue, N.W.
Washington, D.C. 20418 USA

Your comments about the value of these reports are also welcome.

- -

Name ______________________________

Title ______________________________

Institution ______________________________

Street Address ______________________________

____

City ______________________________

Country ____________________ Postal Code __________

64

- -

For More Information

To receive more information about BOSTID reports and programs, please fill in the attached coupon and mail it to:

Board on Science and Technology for International Development
Publications and Information Services (HA–476E)
Office of International Affairs
National Research Council
2101 Constitution Avenue, N.W.
Washington, D.C. 20418 USA

Your comments about the value of these reports are also welcome.

- -

Name ______________________________

Title ______________________________

Institution ______________________________

Street Address ______________________________

____

City ______________________________

Country ____________________ Postal Code __________

64

- -